Touchstones 3

NEW SCHOOL SERIES

Consulting Editor: R. Stone, M.A., A.Inst.P.,
Second Master, Manchester Grammar School
General Editor (Arts): B. A. Phythian, M.A., B.Litt.,
Headmaster, Langley Park School for Boys, Beckenham

Touchstones 3

A TEACHING ANTHOLOGY

M. G. BENTON M.A.
Lecturer, School of Education,
University of Southampton

P. BENTON M.A.
Lecturer, Department of Education,
University of Oxford

HODDER AND STOUGHTON

LONDON SYDNEY AUCKLAND TORONTO

ISBN 0 340 20778 7

First published 1969
Reprinted 1971, 1973 (twice), 1974, 1975, 1978

Printed in Great Britain for
Hodder and Stoughton Educational,
a division of Hodder and Stoughton Ltd,
Mill Road, Dunton Green, Sevenoaks, Kent
by Butler & Tanner Ltd, Frome and London

iv

Foreword

We live in a rapidly changing world; some might say in a too rapidly changing one. Today ideas can alter as much in a decade as in the whole of the preceding century. As the kaleidoscopic patterns of syllabus and method pass before us, it is not always easy to distinguish the important and permanent from the ephemeral. It is our hope that, in the New School Series, we shall be able to produce a group of books which will help colleagues in the classroom, and their pupils, to meet the challenge of the next ten years.

Our main purpose is to provide a wide range of books, covering both the Arts and Sciences at a number of levels, which will allow the teacher increased latitude in his approach, and offer him full scope to develop the creative aspects of his work. It must not be forgotten that the suitability of a particular text for a given form depends largely on the way in which the teacher uses it: the speed and depth of the work will be dictated by the abilities and interests of the pupils rather than by the wishes of the teacher or the nature of the text. Many of the new books will be suitable for all but the lower streams of the comprehensive schools: others will express the newer conceptual, as opposed to factual, approach to teaching, but may be contained within somewhat narrower academic boundaries. We shall be greatly in debt to the many teachers, professional bodies, and others whose untiring efforts have done so much to change the pattern of teaching in recent years. Nor must we forget those pupils who, whether consciously or not, have been the guinea pigs in the experiments which were necessary to prove the new ideas.

We hope to arrange for books to be written by teams of two or more experienced teachers who have tried out the new methods and syllabuses in the classroom, and who will be able to engender in their readers the same enthusiasm which they have instilled into their pupils. It is this dual interest of those who teach and those who are taught which is the key to all successful learning, a process in which we hope to play our part.

R. STONE

Contents

PART A

WORD PICTURES AND IDEAS
Includes:

SENSES AND FEELINGS
Includes:

IMAGES
Includes:

PART B

WORD PICTURES AND IDEAS

x

To the Teacher

The idea of 'teaching poetry' – certainly if the phrase is used in any formal, pedagogic sense – is, in itself, suspect: why, therefore, have we compiled a 'teaching anthology'? Briefly, we felt that there was a need for an anthology which offered more than a collection of poems. Poetry lessons depend so much for their success upon a sympathetic relationship between teacher and pupils and, although books will not in themselves create this relationship, they can help considerably by suggesting ideas for discussion, by showing different approaches to poems, and by encouraging pupils to write poetry themselves. We have attempted to satisfy these needs while avoiding the danger of setting out too rigid a procedure. We hope, too, that the teaching material we include will provide some useful starting-points for teachers looking for fresh ideas.

The pattern of our 'teaching anthology' is as follows. First, in Part A, we introduce three main topics which give information about a particular aspect of poetry, illustrate by examples, point questions and provoke discussion. The individual teacher is the best judge of just how and when to use this area of the book. We anticipate, however, that he might find material for about a dozen lessons in Part A and we have indicated by asterisks where possible sub-divisions of the material might be made. To attempt to structure lessons further than this, we felt, would be too inhibiting to the teacher. Secondly, in Part B, we have grouped the material so that the teacher will be able to deal with several poems, linked by some common quality of technique, subject matter, style or attitude, in any one lesson or sequence of lessons. Thirdly, at the end of most sections in Part B, we have provided a number of suggestions for encouraging the pupils to write their own poems, in the belief that it is just as important to get a child to write poetry as it is to encourage him to appreciate and criticise. We consider that it is vital that pupils should be allowed the chance to write, to experiment, to play with words and sounds, even with the shapes of poems in the same way that they are allowed free expression with paints and plastic materials in an art lesson. Through this kind of personal involvement comes an understanding and appreciation of what they read and, above all, an understanding of themselves and the world around them.

Although we do suggest certain lines of thought, we do not wish the books to be followed slavishly as a 'course'. Indeed, the distinction between material suited, for example, to a third as opposed to a fourth form must sometimes be arbitrary. Although we have numbered our books one to five and have chosen our topics and poems to suit particular age-groups, the teacher will find sufficient flexibility in the arrangement to be able to select and modify the material we print according to his own tastes and the abilities of his pupils.

Creative Writing

There are many ways of stimulating children's writing and every teacher has his own methods. We therefore feel it would be presumptuous to give too much direction and we have, in the main, limited ourselves to suggestions in the creative writing sections. However, we do feel that rather different emphases are needed in the middle-school years: the moodiness and unpredictability which indicate the emotional changes going on in many children of thirteen or fourteen are familiar to all teachers of third year pupils. In the creative writing sections, therefore, as in the anthology, we have aimed at providing material which in several ways will help children to cope with their own growing-up. First, we have made use of their increasing awareness of themselves by inviting them to write poems which require them to sort out their own feelings and attitudes towards experience. Secondly, we have suggested topics for discussion and writing which give children the chance either to show a wider social awareness or to come to terms with more complicated ideas and feelings: the sections on school and war, for instance, should help here. Thirdly, while we would still encourage pupils to write free verse, it is our experience that middle-school children often like the discipline of writing in regular patterns. Using the forms of some of the poems that we anthologise as models for their own verse affords *some* children the satisfaction of having a recognisable pattern of words at which to aim. The manipulation of rhymes, syllables, and metres can help them to define the boundaries of their poems and gives direction to their ideas without sacrificing the original spontaneity and feeling. For others, however, anything more structured than a seventeen syllable haiku proves inhibiting; but, whatever the reaction of the individual pupil to writing in a particular form, there is no doubt that some appreciation of the difficulties of writing in regular patterns is gained and this, in turn, helps the pupil to enjoy poetry more fully as well as become more discriminating in his reading.

The suggested approaches to creative writing are all ones which we have found successful. If teachers wish to pursue the subject of children's writing further, we would recommend the following books: Ted Hughes, *Poetry in the Making*, chapters one to five (Faber); Robert Druce, *The Eye of Innocence* (Brockhampton Press); Brian Powell, *English Through Poetry Writing* (Heinemann); and M. Langdon, *Let the Children Write: An Explanation of Intensive Writing* (Longmans). We have found pictures and photographs invaluable as 'starters', particularly in that they focus attention on detail and help children to *see* as well as to look. We hope that teachers will also use other stimuli – e.g. music, or objects brought in by pupils and teacher – when appropriate. Large and colourful reproductions of paintings can be useful; abstracts as much as more representational works often fire the imagination. Paintings by Kandinsky and Miró have been found particularly successful. There are also many good photographs available in magazines and colour supplements which are easily mounted and may be used as starting-points for original writing. A file of these will grow rapidly.

The introduction of unusual and interesting objects may help to develop awareness and sharpen the senses – making writing more detailed, more exact, and, above all, more spontaneous. It is likely that most teachers already use this method, but it may be of interest to note some of the objects that we have found to arouse a strong response: driftwood, oddly-shaped branches, twigs, roots and tubers are all particularly effective both visually and in stimulating a desire to *touch*. Textures are often strongly felt and pebbles, shells, conkers and bones may also be used primarily for the tactile response, though there is obviously much else besides.

With the co-operation of the Biology department, skulls, bones, skeletons and living creatures may be borrowed and studied in detail. Leaves, feathers and pine-cones are other natural objects which have fascinating structures and are easily obtainable. Lighted sparklers have also proved a successful device. All senses are brought into play here – one can even taste the faintly acrid smoke – and a real firework, however tame, evokes many memories of bonfire night. Soap bubbles, as produced by those canisters of bubble mixture into which a wire ring is dipped, are beautiful to look at, move in an unpredictable fashion and vanish in a most satisfying way. There is no reason, of course, why all these stimuli – particularly the visual material – should not be used as a basis for prose writing as well as for poems.

A final word: poems cannot be written on demand and we would emphasise that in using the Creative Writing sections teachers should encourage discussion of our suggestions and not present them to the class as 'exercises' which must be completed. Our own open-ended questions in these sections are not meant in any way to dictate the nature of the pupil's response: they provide stimuli which the pupil should feel free to ignore if he so chooses, or to adapt in the light of his own experience.

M. G. B.
P. B.

PART A

WORD-PICTURES AND IDEAS

Day-dreams, private thoughts, personal feelings about people or places or incidents are things that often we tend to guard from others. In protecting these innermost thoughts and feelings we feel we are protecting our real 'self', the things which make each of us unique, the things which mean that we have a very different view of ourselves from the one that our closest friends or even our parents have of us. Have you ever really thought about yourself? Not simply about the external things such as the colour of your hair or the type of clothes you like to wear – but about the things which really matter to you? Particular loves or hates, your relationships with your friends and family, experiences which have meant something to you – everyone has some things which are important to them. Often these things are easy to identify but difficult to understand: for example, you might well say you love your parents but find it hard to know just what you mean by this. Or you might feel that, say, a serious illness has been an important experience for you and yet not be sure of the reasons. Poetry can help you understand your confused feelings.

When you read and discuss other writers' poems or, even more so, when you write your own pieces, you are concerned with experiences that have mattered to someone. For poems are attempts to capture in words moments of personal importance. One type of poem which concentrates entirely on such moments is the Japanese haiku poem. As you will see from the following examples haiku are short, three-line poems which, because of their shortness, cannot afford a lot of detail; what detail there is has to be significant and important to the writer. Here is a mother writing about the death of her little boy.

I Wonder

I wonder in what fields today
He chases dragonflies in play,
My little boy – who ran away.

CHIYO*

At first this may seem to be just a simple word-picture, but if you think about the words the mother uses, two questions may occur to you.

What idea does the mother have of where her child has gone?

Why does she say that he 'ran away'?

Although this is a very simply expressed haiku, we can, nevertheless, get an insight into the writer's thoughts and feelings about an important moment in her life.

Haiku are not complicated poems technically. In the original Japanese, haiku are seventeen-syllable poems, the syllables being arranged 5, 7, 5 on the three lines: in translation, however, it is not always possible to keep to this syllable pattern and often the translator has chosen to use rhymes instead to give the poems a definite shape, as you can see from the poem above. You will understand the syllabic pattern if you compare the following two poems. Both are about rain: the first is a translation, the second is by an English writer.

Springtime Rain

Springtime rain: together,
Intent upon their talking, go
Straw-raincoat and umbrella.

BUSON

*Unless otherwise stated, all haiku in this volume are translations by Harold G. Henderson in his book *An Introduction to Haiku* (Doubleday Anchor, New York, 1958).

Rain Haiku

Gentle summer rain;
Scratch, scratch upon the window
With its little stick.

COLIN ROWBOTHAM

Once you are sure you understand the arrangement of syllables in haiku, try to write one or two of your own. The choice of subject is up to you, but remember that you will write best about something which matters to you: it may not be as important as the death of a loved one; perhaps just the record of a moment which you found interesting or significant.

*

The thoughts expressed in a poem always seem different from the thoughts we put into words each day in speaking or even from the thoughts we write in an essay or letter. Poems do not always explain feelings and ideas; they capture them. Here are two more haiku.

Flower-Viewing

On top of skeletons
They put a gala dress, and then –
The flower-viewing!

ONITSURA

The Apprentice Priestling

A boy not ten years old
They are giving to the temple!
Oh, it's cold!

SHIKI

5

Do you think the writer regards the flower-viewing festival simply as a happy occasion?
What does the writer feel about the fate of the young boy in the second poem?
The situation and thought of a poem are quite often left unexplained, for the poet wants his words to represent what an experience meant to him: his poem must try to recreate the experience. The next poem does this.

In a Station of the Metro

The apparition of these faces in the crowd;
Petals on a wet, black bough.

EZRA POUND

Little is actually stated, but a good deal is suggested.
What is the connection between the first line and the second?
Why does the poet use the word 'apparition'?
This poem was arrived at after a lot of hard work on a much longer version of the same idea. The poet's job was to prune away unnecessary words so that his finished poem would represent, in this sharp, uncluttered way, the experience of seeing a crowd of people in an underground station. Again, making every word contribute to the word-picture is something that you will not understand properly unless you attempt it yourself. Try to write a few lines which capture vividly and precisely any scene that sticks in your mind: it might be a sunset or a gasworks. Whatever you choose, when you have a first draft of, say, five or six lines, try cutting away the unnecessary lines or phrases until you have two or three lines which express exactly what you want. You may well try to use a comparison as Ezra Pound has done.

*

You will already be familiar with the fact that poets often convey what they see and feel by the use of comparisons. Similarly, when a poet wants to express his thoughts, he may well compare one idea with another, or present several ideas in one poem because they are associated by some common factor. Read the following poem carefully and discuss what the thoughts of the poet are.

Nothing Gold can Stay

Nature's first green is gold,
Her hardest hue to hold.
Her early leaf's a flower;
But only so an hour.
Then leaf subsides to leaf.
So Eden sank to grief,
So dawn goes down to day.
Nothing gold can stay.

ROBERT FROST

You may find it easiest to think of the poem in two halves.
In the first four lines the poet is describing something that he has noticed: what?
In the second half of the poem the poet develops certain thoughts. Can you put them into your own words?
Here is another poem which develops in the same way: first, a simple word-picture, then an idea.

A Priest

A little liked, more feared, his dark
    Black-coated way he goes.
His chin is strong, his eyebrows meet
    Thickly above his nose.

And who can tell, so grimly schooled,
    Such lord of self he seems,
If devils that are mute by day
    Assail him in his dreams?

L. A. G. STRONG

What picture do you have of the priest in your mind's eye?
What idea does the writer express in verse 2?

Writing poetry in this way is more difficult for you are being asked
to use your imagination both to create a carefully observed word-
picture and also to include any thoughts which come into your
mind as a result. Again you have complete freedom as to choice
of subject, but try in the first half of your poem to capture clearly
and exactly a particular person or scene; then, in the second half,
you may be able to deepen the ideas of your poem by including
thoughts which your description suggests and which, to *you*, seem
of importance.

SENSES AND FEELINGS

Most living creatures, ourselves included, rely on five Senses to give them information about the world around them. What are these Senses? Which of them is most important to you and which matters least? Although you may not agree as to which is the least important, it is almost certain that the ability to see matters most to you. A poet is trying to create pictures in your mind: he wants you to see something exactly as he sees it, and, even more important, he wants you to feel what he feels. What kind of feeling is the writer trying to give us in these lines?

> A puff-adder, khaki,
> fatter than a stocking of pus
> except for its short thin tail . . .
>
> (from *Leviathan* by DOUGLAS LIVINGSTONE)

The picture is clear enough; we can see the snake clearly in the mind's eye, but this is not all. Why is the picture so sickening? What senses does it make us use?

Here is another snake:

> He reached down from a fissure in the earth-wall in the gloom
> And trailed his yellow-brown slackness soft-bellied down, over
>   the edge of the stone trough
> And rested his throat upon the stone bottom,
> And where the water had dripped from the tap, in a small clear-
>   ness,
> He sipped with his straight mouth,
> Softly drank through his straight gums, into his slack long body,
> Silently.
>
> (from *Snake* by D. H. LAWRENCE)

9

Again, the picture is vivid but here we not only see the snake but we also *feel* its movement as it eases its body smoothly down to the water, slithering across the earth-wall. If you read the passage aloud you find that you *become* the snake and that you imitate the snake not only in the way he moves but even in the way he drinks, sipping the water so precisely and efficiently. How does Lawrence make us react in this way?

Sight then, giving the reader a clear picture, is very important but it is only one of your senses and you need to have them all finely tuned and keenly aware if you are to involve the reader in what you are writing. Sight, hearing, touch, smell, taste are our senses but most of us, unfortunately, use only one or perhaps two of them in our attempts to describe things we have seen and felt. When you do see or visualise a scene it is often helpful to concentrate on details as Elizabeth Bishop does when she describes a tremendous fish that she has caught. He is very real:

> He hung a grunting weight,
> battered and venerable
> and homely. Here and there
> his brown skin hung in strips
> like ancient wall-paper,
> and its pattern of darker brown
> was like wall-paper:
> shapes like full-blown roses
> stained and lost through age.
> He was speckled with barnacles,
> fine rosettes of lime,
> and infested
> with tiny white sea-lice,
> and underneath two or three
> rags of green weed hung down.

You can read the whole poem on p. 114 and throughout its length there is the same minute attention to detail. In the lines quoted above what details make a strong impression and make you feel that this is a writer who has seen what she is describing and really knows what she is talking about?

*

11

Sound we have dealt with at greater length in an earlier book and it often plays a very important part in building up the clear picture you wish to convey. Imagine, for example, that you too are writing about a snake working its way across the grass towards you. You notice its appearance, its colour and markings, the way the grass divides and closes as he passes, but you need not stop just there. Listen to the sound his movement makes.

What sounds does he make as he slides through grass?

As he moves over dry leaves?

Over dry and crumbling earth?

Is there any sound made intentionally by the creature?

Use your other senses too.

What would he be like to touch?

What is the texture of his skin like?

Is his body warm or cold?

Touch, as you will realise, is one of our strongest senses and can evoke a very strong response in the reader.

In this present example the senses of smell and taste are both rather out of place and they generally play a less important part than the other three senses but, given the right subject, they can be just as striking. You can probably think of several subjects where these senses would be as important as sight or touch. One experience most of you will have had is your first visit to the school science laboratories – perhaps as a first former when everything at your school was new and exciting and entering a full-sized laboratory with all its equipment was like entering a new world.

What were your first impressions as you entered?

What sights, sounds and smells hit your senses?

Can you find words for the *taste* of some smells?

Are the chemistry and biology labs. different in any way?

Do you remember . . . bottles of strange chemicals arranged in rows? . . . the cones of flame on the bunsen burners? . . . tall stools and long benches? . . . strange shaped retorts and glass-ware? . . .

Perhaps you can write a poem which captures something of the excitement. Try to be alive to all the tiny detailed sense impressions that we so often ignore and you will find that your writing will be far more convincing.

Through the information supplied by your senses come feeling and understanding for what you are writing about.

Why, you might ask yourself, do I shudder at the thought of a snake's skin against my own?

What is so pleasing about lazing, eyes closed, in the sunshine on a hot day?

What sort of feelings do you experience during a particularly exhilarating ride on a big-dipper?

Again, you could perhaps write a poem about one of these, trying to capture in detail what all your senses register and what your feelings are.

*

Feelings are often difficult to explain and sometimes unexpected. Why, for example, do people *enjoy* watching a tragic play or reading a sad book or poem? Is *enjoy* the right word? Perhaps part of the answer might be found in the woman who leaves a cinema, tears running down her cheeks after watching a very sad film: 'I do so like a good cry,' she says. The next week she might be at a wedding, tears flowing just as fast, and explain, 'I always cry when I'm very happy'. In fact, we all enjoy exercising our emotions – perhaps even wallowing in them like the woman in the cinema. We enjoy hating the villain, sharing the hero's daring, being frightened by a horror film.

Our feelings need exercise otherwise they weaken and wither away or go soft and flabby. Try, in your own writing, to understand exactly what you feel and why you feel as you do; above all, try to be honest. It is no good writing what you think you ought to feel or what you think your teacher might like you to feel: your poems are *you* or they are nothing. Feeling does not mean wallowing in emotion, neither does it mean being 'poetic'. You know the sort of thing – where, for example, all trees become 'majestic', where every daffodil is greeted with rapturous squeals of delight simply because this is thought to be the 'poetic' way of reacting to nature. A poem is not made by dressing up emptiness in fine-sounding words and throwing in a few 'o'ers and e'ers'. There should not be a special 'soppy' language reserved for use in poems and the best poetry even when it is about 'traditional' subjects – nature, animals, love, religion, for example – is never soft. Look at D. H. Lawrence's fish:

Unhooked his gorping, water-horny mouth,
And seen his horror-tilted eye,
His red-gold, water-precious, mirror-flat bright eye;
And felt him beat in my hand, with his mucous, leaping life-
    throb.

There is no slackness there and the experience of holding the live
fish in the hand is something that we can share because it is obvious
that this man knows what it is like and has felt it himself. In the
following lines taken from William Blake's *Auguries of Innocence* the
language is very simple. Do you think the poet's aims are helped by
this simplicity?

A robin redbreast in a cage
Puts all Heaven in a rage.

A horse misused upon the road
Calls to Heaven for human blood.

Each outcry of the hunted hare
A fibre from the brain does tear.

Simple it may be, but there is no doubt that Blake felt very deeply
about his subject.

Our emotions are rarely as simple as we might think, and some –
love or sorrow, for example – can be very unpredictable. You can
'love' money or rice-pudding, a girl or boy-friend, a parent, the
family dog: but it is to be hoped that you do not mean the same thing
each time you talk of loving one of these! Words are often very
imprecise and often we use them unthinkingly in this kind of way.
Try to think carefully about your feelings before you label them with
one of these over-simple shorthand words – you may find your
feelings quite different from what you might expect them to be. The
writer of the next poem perhaps discovered this.

The Lesson

'Your father's gone,' my bald headmaster said.
His shiny dome and brown tobacco jar
Splintered at once in tears. It wasn't grief.
I cried for knowledge which was bitterer
Than any grief. For there and then I knew
That grief has uses – that a father dead
Could bind the bully's fist a week or two;
And then I cried for shame, then for relief.

I was a month past ten when I learnt this:
I still remember how the noise was stilled
In school-assembly when my grief came in.
Some goldfish in a bowl quietly sculled
Around their shining prison on its shelf.
They were indifferent. All the other eyes
Were turned towards me. Somewhere in myself
Pride, like a goldfish, flashed a sudden fin.

                    EDWARD LUCIE-SMITH

What is the boy's *first* feeling when he hears of his father's death?
Why is this?
What feelings follow his initial response?
Why should he be proud?
    Although these feelings are not perhaps those we might expect a
child to feel at the death of a parent, it is clear that this was in fact
what happened and that the poet is being quite honest. Perhaps you
can think of an occasion when you have not in fact felt as you
thought you *should* feel – the death of a relative or a pet perhaps;
success or failure in something that mattered greatly to you; your
reaction to news of a tragedy or to an Oxfam advertisement. Try to
write about it and explain how you felt.

                    *

    In your writing try to avoid the 'stock response'. What do you
think this phrase means and why do you think it is to be avoided?
You may remember D. H. Lawrence's poem *Bat* where he gradually

realises that the graceful and pleasing swallows that he has been watching fly in and out of the bridge arches have given way to bats. Immediately his feelings change to those of revulsion and horror and he can see the bats only as loathesome creatures,

> Creatures that hang themselves up like an old rag, to sleep;
> And disgustingly upside down.
> Hanging upside down like rows of disgusting old rags
> And grinning in their sleep.
> Bats!

The bats have done him no harm: why do you think he feels like this? Would your feelings be the same if you were in a similar situation? Perhaps you could write a poem on one of the many other creatures we often regard as repulsive. Try to picture it clearly in your mind and examine every detail, using all your senses. Try to put down exactly what you see and feel and ask yourself why you feel as you do. Are your feelings justified? Different people have different pet-hates but here are some of the more common ones: spiders, rats, worms, slugs, snakes, flies, frogs, toads, earwigs, beetles.

Although you can express your feelings directly and perhaps violently if you feel the subject warrants such treatment, this is not the only way:

The Bird

When I got home
Last night I found
A bird the cat
Had brought into the house
On the kitchen floor.

It wasn't dead.
It looked as if
It was, at first.
There were some feathers lying
Against the wall:

16

The bird itself
With its wings folded
Lay and stared.
It didn't move.
I picked it up:

Quivering like a clockwork
Toy in my hand
I carried it out
Into the yard
And put it down

In a slice of light
From the door. I lifted
A long broom
By the handle near to
The head and struck

The bird four times.
The fourth time it
Didn't move.
Blood, in a stringy
Trickle, blotched

The white concrete.
I edged the remains
Up with a red
Plastic shovel.
Lifting it through

The house to the cellar
I tipped it out
In the dust-bin along with
Snakes of fluff
And empty soup-tins.

When I emptied the tea-leaves
This morning I saw
The bird I killed
Leaning its head
On a broken egg-shell.

GEORGE MACBETH

The tone of the poem seems to be rather matter-of-fact: do you think the writer is cold, even callous about the bird? Why do you think he chooses this particularly 'flat' style of writing?

Through feeling comes understanding. Perhaps this poem by the Chinese writer Yuan Mei best expresses much of what we have tried to say.

Only be willing to search for poetry, and there will be poetry:
My soul, a tiny speck, is my tutor.
Evening sun and fragrant grass are common things,
But, with understanding, they can become glorious verse.

(*Expression of feelings, VII.*
trans. R. KOTEWALL and N. L. SMITH)

IMAGES

If you use a camera you will know how important it is to look first through the viewfinder and think about your picture before you release the shutter: if you become 'snap-happy' and simply shoot without thinking, the chances are that your pictures will be rather dull. Think for a moment about what you are trying to do when you look through the viewfinder. You move the camera slightly, you perhaps change the angle of the shot and eventually you are satisfied and the picture is taken. What sort of things make you dissatisfied with the first picture you see in the viewfinder? Why do you move the camera about? What sort of things make you think to yourself 'This is it; it looks best like this.'?

A good photographer has his own special way of seeing; he is trained to use his eyes, to look for pictures hidden in everything around us. He has a special talent that can make us stop and look again at things we may have seen thousands of times before. You would perhaps not think your breakfast table a subject for a great photograph or a great painting, but, given the right man behind the camera, given the artist who can see, then even such everyday objects as plates, cups and saucers, the milk jug and the teapot can be made into a satisfying picture. The painting by Melendez over-leaf shows us what can be done in this way: perhaps you could do a twentieth century 'word-painting' on the same subject.

What objects stand out on your own breakfast or dinner table? Which shapes catch your eye? How are they arranged? Does the light reflect from some surfaces and not others? Look at the different textures – the tablecloth ... china ... pottery ... plastic ... wood ... Describe in a poem what you see.

The photographer, the painter, the poet, tend to see things in a different way from the majority of us who are often too busy to spend our time composing pictures from the world around us. Just as you have done in writing your poem, they also say, 'Stop! Have you noticed this? I like the shape of this bottle ... Look at this chair ... What a curious face ...' and so on. William Carlos Williams paints a clear, striking picture in this poem.

19

A Negro Woman

carrying a bunch of marigolds
    wrapped
        in an old newspaper:
She carries them upright,
    bareheaded,
        the bulk
of her thighs
    causing her to waddle
        as she walks
looking into
    the store window which she passes
        on her way.
What is she
    but an ambassador
        from another world
a world of pretty marigolds
    of two shades
        which she announces
not knowing what she does
    other
        than walk the streets
holding the flowers upright
    as a torch
        so early in the morning.

There she is, a picture caught in words, a simple, bold and colourful personality.

*

An image is a picture, a way of seeing, and a poet is a dealer in images. One technique frequently used by poets, particularly when they want to convey an image of something abstract, is that of personification. Here is Spenser's picture of Despair:

That darkesome cave they enter, where they find
   That cursed man, low sitting on the ground,
   Musing full sadly in his sullen mind;
   His greasy locks, long growen, and unbound,
   Disordered hung about his shoulders round,
   And hid his face; through which his hollow eyne[1]   [1]eyes
   Looked deadly dull, and stared as astound;
   His raw-bone cheeks through penury and pine,
Were shrunk into his jaws, as he did never dine.

His garment nought but many ragged clouts,
   With thorns together pinned and patched was,
   The which his naked sides he wrapped about;
   And him beside there lay upon the grass
   A dreary corpse, whose life away did pass,
   And wallowed in his own yet lukewarm blood,
   That from his wound still welled fresh alas;
   In which a rusty knife fast fixed stood,
And made an open passage for the gushing flood.

and here is Gluttony:

And by his side rode loathsome *Gluttony*,
   Deformed creature, on a filthy swine,
   His belly was up-blow with luxury,
   And eke with fatness swollen were his eyne,
   And like a crane his neck was long and fine,
   With which he swallowed up excessive feast,
   For want whereof poor people oft did pine,
   And all the way, most like a brutish beast,
He spewed up his gorge, that all did him deteast.

In green vine leaves he was right fitly clad;
   For other clothes he could not wear for heat,
   And on his head an ivy garland had,
   From under which fast trickled down the sweat:
   Still as he rode, he somewhat still did eat,
   And in his hand did bear a boozing can,
   Of which he supped so oft, that on his seat
   His drunken corpse he scarce upholden can,
In shape and life more like a monster, than a man.

22

Unfit he was for any worldly thing,
  And eke unable once to stir or go,
  Nor fit to be of counsel to a king,
  Whose mind in meat and drink was drowned so,
  That from his friend he seldom knew his foe:
  Full of disease was his carcass blew,
  And a dry dropsy through his flesh did flow:
  Which by misdiet daily greater grew:
Such one was *Gluttony*, the second of that crew.

What do you think 'personification' means? How might Arcimboldo's painting *Winter,* on the previous page, be described as a personification? Perhaps you could write your own modern personification of an abstract. Here are some ideas for you: Hate, War, Love, Envy, Anger, Fear, Spring, Winter . . . There are many more from which you could choose and obviously if you choose the last suggestion you could use many of the details in the painting.

*

Comparison is one of the most common methods used by writers to give us a clear picture of what it is they see and feel. In his poem *Wind* Ted Hughes is constantly comparing things.

This house has been far out at sea all night,
The woods crashing through darkness, the booming hills,
Winds stampeding the fields under the window
Floundering black astride and blinding wet

Till day rose; then under an orange sky
The hills had new places, and wind wielded
Blade-light, luminous black and emerald,
Flexing like the lens of a mad eye.

At noon I scaled along the house-side as far as
The coal-house door. I dared once to look up –
Through the brunt wind that dented the balls of my eyes
The tent of the hills drummed and strained its guyrope,

The fields quivering, the skyline a grimace,
At any second to bang and vanish with a flap:
The wind flung a magpie away and a black-
Back gull bent like an iron bar slowly. The house

Rang like some fine green goblet in the note
That any second would shatter it. Now deep
In chairs, in front of the great fire, we grip
Our hearts and cannot entertain book, thought,

Or each other. We watch the fire blazing,
And feel the roots of the house move, but sit on,
Seeing the window tremble to come in,
Hearing the stones cry out under the horizons.

What do you think he means by the first line?
What is the 'tent of the hills'?
What do you think Ted Hughes means when he talks of a black-
back gull which 'bent like an iron bar slowly'?
Some of these comparisons are direct; for example, the house is
'*like* some fine green goblet'. In others, however, the word 'like'
does not appear although the poet is in fact making a kind of comparison; for instance, when he writes of 'the tent of the hills'. These
comparisons, these images, help the poet to give us a clearer, more
vivid picture, and of course, they make us use our imaginations.
Some of Hughes' images in this poem are unusual and it is worth
spending some time discussing just what he is trying to convey and
whether you think he does it successfully or not.

*

When one discusses images in detail it is curious to find that
they often mean different things to different people. In each of
the following extracts the writer has captured his subject in an
original way by using comparisons.

(1) A waterfall
It appears an athletic glacier
Has reared into reverse: is swallowed up
And regurgitated through this long throat.
SEAMUS HEANEY

(2) A docker
There, in the corner, staring at his drink.
The cap juts like a gantry's crossbeam,
Cowling plated forehead and sledgehead jaw.
Speech is clamped in the lips' vice.
SEAMUS HEANEY

(3) A kangaroo
Her little loose hands, and drooping Victorian shoulders,
And then her great weight below the waist, her vast
    pale belly
With a thin young yellow little paw hanging out, and
    straggle of a long thin ear, like ribbon,
Like a funny trimming to the middle of her belly, thin
    little dangle of an immature paw, and one thin ear.
D. H. LAWRENCE

(4) The imprint of a sea-shell on a stone
And chiselled clear on stone
A spider-web of shell,
The thumb-print of the sea.
N. NICHOLSON

(5) A stagnant pond in a city
Daily it sweltered in the punishing sun.
Bubbles gargled delicately, bluebottles
Wove a strong gauze of sound around the smell.
SEAMUS HEANEY

26

(6) Fog

The yellow fog that rubs its back upon the window-panes,
The yellow smoke that rubs its muzzle on the window-panes
Licked its tongue into the corners of the evening,
Lingered upon the pools that stand in drains,
Let fall upon its back the soot that falls from chimneys,
Slipped by the terrace, made a sudden leap,
And seeing that it was a soft October night,
Curled once about the house, and fell asleep.

T. S. ELIOT

(7) Thistle

Thistle, blue bunch of daggers
rattling upon the wind,
saw-tooth that separates
the lips of grasses.

LAURIE LEE

(8) Pigeons

Small blue busybodies
Strutting like fat gentlemen
With hands clasped
Under their swallowtail coats

RICHARD KELL

(9) Ice

Ice
Has got its spearhead into place.

First a skin, delicately here
Restraining a ripple from the air;

Soon plate and rivet on pond and brook;
Then tons of chain and massive lock

To hold rivers . . .

TED HUGHES

(10) A schoolboy
Timothy Winters comes to school
With eyes as wide as a football-pool,
Ears like bombs and teeth like splinters:
A blitz of a boy is Timothy Winters.

CHARLES CAUSLEY

(11) Storm in the Black Forest
Now it is almost night, from the bronzey soft sky
jugfull after jugfull of pure white liquid fire, bright white
tipples over and spills down,
and is gone
and gold-bronze flutters bent through the thick upper air.

And as the electric liquid pours out, sometimes
a still brighter white snake wriggles among it, spilled
and tumbling wriggling down the sky:

D. H. LAWRENCE

Which of these images did you find most effective and why?
Which ones do you not *see* at all?

In discussing these images *do* you find that they mean different things to different members of the class?

You may be able to think of comparisons for some of the following and write two or three lines of free verse where you use them: petrol or oil on the surface of a puddle, the surface of your desk, electricity pylons, the London underground. These are only suggestions; find your own subjects if you can.

*

In the next poem the writer has created several images – just as you have been attempting to do – each of which helps the reader see more clearly what is being described.

28

Cow in Calf

It seems she has swallowed a barrel.
From forelegs to haunches
her belly is slung like a hammock.

Slapping her out of the byre is like slapping
a great bag of seed. My hand
tingled as if strapped, but I had to
hit her again and again and
heard the blows plump like a depth-charge
far in her gut.

The udder grows. Windbags
of bagpipes are crammed there
to drone in her lowing.
Her cud and her milk, her heats and her calves
keep coming and going.

SEAMUS HEANEY

What impression of the cow do you get from the first line?
What picture do you see in your mind's eye from lines 2 & 3?
What do the cow and a 'great bag of seed' (l. 5) have in common?
Why 'windbags of bagpipes' (l. 10–11)?
All these comparisons, although very different from each other, seem to be used by the writer to capture one particular quality of the cow in calf. Can you put this overall impression into your own words?

So far you have read and written images which are brief – probably of no more than two or three lines. The poem which follows, however, will show you a writer sustaining a comparison all the way through his poem, elaborating it in detail at the beginning, reminding us of it indirectly in the middle, and returning to it in an unusual way at the end.

The Oak Tree

The oak tree thrust its fist
Through the brown-paper wrapping of dry soil,
Letting light into the earth. Its wrist
Was rigged with segs, and stems of ivy
Wound varicose veins around the arm.
It opened its hand and birds flew to the fingers
As falcons to a falconer. A charm
Of chaffinch and linnet made tingle the thumbs of winter,
Spring brought gloves of green,
Summer itched with flies, and autumn
Doled out and dropped its pennies for the squirrels,
And the knuckles were wide to the wind. The lean
Old men goggled from the woods – brown snouts
Peeked from ferns. Dandelions
Feathered their beards with seeds, and bramble knouts
Whipped their leather thighs, but they never felt them.
They shuffled up to the shins through paddock-stools and
    cow-pats,
And stood in a circle round the tree.
The oldest of them all (his beard
Draggled the ground like a weeping willow)
Touched never a stick, but three
Dropped the tree along the line he measured,
Lopped and topped the branches and ripped the bark off,
Till the wet trunk lay bare as a skinned rabbit. He
Drew out the pith and marrow of the log
And planed it thin as plywood. Shavings
Clog-danced on the cobbles, and yellow sawdust
Pollened the October grass.
He took the wood and bent it
Gently as a surgeon setting a broken bone,
But quick with a crack and a splitting of the spine
It snapped and lay dead in his hands. For a space he held it,
Surprised and sad, then (one arm pointing
Across the field to another tree) he threw it
Into a heaped fire of dead leaves
The men had kindled there. The tossed wood

Fell deep in the damp smoulder, till the slow smoke
Pushed up its fingers, gripping the skirts of the air.
And the hand of the fire was the hand of the living oak.

NORMAN NICHOLSON

What is the image which is developed through the first twelve lines? Discuss the details carefully: you may prefer some to others.

Although the middle part of the poem describes the old men felling the oak, we are still reminded of the original image in one or two places. Where?

What happens to the comparison in the last few lines?

PART B

WORD-PICTURES AND IDEAS

The Poor Man's Son

Poverty's child –
he starts to grind the rice,
and gazes at the moon.

BASHO

The Weeping Willow

How strong a green
are the strings of willow branches:
the flowing of the stream!

ONITSURA

A Wish

I'd like enough drinks
to put me to sleep – on stones
covered with pinks.

BASHO

The Cuckoo's Song

As the cuckoo flies,
its singing stretches out:
upon the water lies.

BASHO

City People

Townsfolk, it is plain –
carrying red maple leaves
in the homebound train.

MEISETSU

The Dragonfly

The dragonfly:
his face is very nearly
only eye!

CHISOKU

Constancy

Though it be broken –
broken again – still it's there:
the moon on the water.

CHOSHU

The Red Cockatoo

Sent as a present from Annam –
A red cockatoo.
Coloured like the peach-tree blossom,
Speaking with the speech of men.
And they did to it what is always done
To the learned and eloquent.
They took a cage with stout bars
And shut it up inside.

PO CHU-I
(*Trans. Arthur Waley*)

Cock-Crow

Out of the wood of thoughts that grows by night
To be cut down by the sharp axe of light, –
Out of the night, two cocks together crow,
Cleaving the darkness with a silver blow:
And bright before my eyes twin trumpeters stand,
Heralds of splendour, one at either hand,
Each facing each as in a coat of arms:
The milkers lace their boots up at the farms.

EDWARD THOMAS

Liu Ch'e

The rustling of the silk is discontinued,
Dust drifts over the court-yard,
There is no sound of footfall, and the leaves
Scurry into heaps and lie still,
And she the rejoicer of the heart is beneath them:

A wet leaf that clings to the threshold.

EZRA POUND

Fan-Piece, for her Imperial Lord

O fan of white silk,
    clear as frost on the grass-blade,
You also are laid aside.

EZRA POUND

The Falling Flower

In the lamplight's vermilion shade
The dark red peony unfolds
Its hundred-petalled fans.
The fire's coral breath unloads
In a random shower
This quietly exploding rose.

Slowly the stillness
Lets handfuls of petals fall.
On the pink-checked tablecloth
Softly the flower pounces,
Weighing this dying hour
In its own crimson ounces.

JAMES KIRKUP

Fallen Flower

Fallen flower I see
Returning to its branch –
Ah! a butterfly.

A. MORITAKE
(*Trans. G. Bownas and A. Thwaite*)

Flower Dump

Cannas shiny as slag,
Slug-soft stems,
Whole beds of bloom pitched on a pile,
Carnations, verbenas, cosmos,
Moulds, weeds, dead leaves,
Turned-over roots
With bleached veins
Twined like fine hair,
Each clump in the shape of a pot;
Everything limp
But one tulip on top,
One swaggering head
Over the dying, the newly dead.

THEODORE ROETHKE

Ts'ai Chi'h

The petals fall in the fountain,
   the orange-coloured rose-leaves,
Their ochre clings to the stone.

EZRA POUND

To Paint a Water Lily

A green level of lily leaves
Roofs the pond's chamber and paves

The flies' furious arena: study
These, the two minds of this lady.

41

First observe the air's dragonfly
That eats meat, that bullets by

Or stands in space to take aim;
Others as dangerous comb the hum

Under the trees. There are battle-shouts
And death-cries everywhere hereabouts

But inaudible, so the eyes praise
To see the colours of these flies

Rainbow their arcs, spark, or settle
Cooling like beads of molten metal

Through the spectrum. Think what worse
Is the pond-bed's matter of course;

Prehistoric bedragonned times
Crawl that darkness with Latin names,

Have evolved no improvements there,
Jaws for heads, the set stare,

Ignorant of age as of hour –
Now paint the long-necked lily-flower

Which, deep in both worlds, can be still
As a painting, trembling hardly at all

Though the dragonfly alight,
Whatever horror nudge her root.

TED HUGHES

To Paint the Portrait of a Bird

To Elsa Henriquez

First paint a cage
with an open door
then paint
something pretty
something simple
something beautiful
something useful . . .
for the bird
then place the canvas against a tree
in a garden
in a wood
or in a forest
hide behind the tree
without speaking
without moving . . .
Sometimes the bird comes quickly
but he can just as well spend long years
before deciding
Don't get discouraged
wait
wait years if necessary
the swiftness or slowness of the coming
of the bird having no rapport
with the success of the picture
When the bird comes
if he comes
observe the most profound silence
wait till the bird enters the cage
and when he has entered
gently close the door with a brush
then
paint out all the bars one by one

taking care not to touch any of the feathers of the bird
Then paint the portrait of the tree
choosing the most beautiful of its branches
for the bird
paint also the green foliage and the wind's freshness
the dust of the sun
and the noise of the insects in the summer heat
and then wait for the bird to decide to sing
If the bird doesn't sing
it's a bad sign
a sign that the painting is bad
but if he sings it's a good sign
a sign that you can sign
So then so very gently you pull out
one of the feathers of the bird
and you write your name in the corner of the picture.

JACQUES PRÉVERT

(*Trans. Lawrence Ferlinghetti*)

The Happy Boy

It is the son of tears and want
Who learns to make the future grow,
The circle at the tunnel's end.
But the entirely happy child
Becomes a loiterer all his life,
Looking for the private glade
And the lost dell where he played.

JAMES REEVES

The Optimist

The optimist builds himself safe inside a cell
and paints the inside walls sky-blue
and blocks up the door
and says he's in heaven.

D. H. LAWRENCE

From a Boat at Coniston

I look into the lake (the lacquered water
Black with the sunset), watching my own face.
Tiny red-ribbed fishes swim
In and out of the nostrils, long-tongued weeds
Lick at the light that oozes down from the surface,
And bubbles rise from the eyes like aerated
Tears shed there in the element of mirrors.
My sight lengthens its focus; sees the sky
Laid level upon the glass, the loud
World of the wind and the map-making clouds
    and history
Squinting over the rim of the fell. The wind
Lets on the water, paddling like a duck,
And face and cloud are grimaced out
In inch-deep wrinkles of the moving waves.
A blackbird clatters; alder leaves
Make mooring buoys for the water beetles.
I wait for the wind to drop, against hope
Hoping, and against the weather, yet to see
The water empty, the water full of itself,
Free of the sky and the cloud and free of me.

NORMAN NICHOLSON

A Last Narcissus

Clearing a little space between
The broad leaves of the lily-pond,
He saw the golden fishes move like thoughts
Behind his inquiring eyes'
Reflected inquiries.

He saw his own clear face
That did not seem to look.
In trees around his head, bird-fishes hung.
He smiled, and from an open book,
His lips, a toad put out its tongue.

JAMES KIRKUP

Water Picture

In the pond in the park
all things are doubled:
Long buildings hang and
wriggle gently. Chimneys
are bent legs bouncing
on clouds below. A flag
wags like a fishhook
down there in the sky.

The arched stone bridge
is an eye, with underlid
in the water. In its lens
dip crinkled heads with hats
that don't fall off. Dogs go by,
barking on their backs.
A baby, taken to feed the
ducks, dangles upside-down,
a pink balloon for a buoy.

Treetops deploy a haze of
cherry bloom for roots,
where birds coast belly-up
in the glass bowl of a hill;
from its bottom a bunch
of peanut-munching children
is suspended by their
sneakers, waveringly.

A swan, with twin necks
forming the figure three,
steers between two dimpled
towers doubled. Fondly
hissing, she kisses herself,
and all the scene is troubled:
water-windows splinter,
tree-limbs tangle, the bridge
folds like a fan.

MAY SWENSON

Corner Seat

Suspended in a moving night
The face in the reflected train
Looks at first sight as self-assured
As your own face – But look again:
Windows between you and the world
Keep out the cold, keep out the fright;
Then why does your reflection seem
So lonely in the moving night?

LOUIS MACNEICE

Reflections

The mirror above my fireplace reflects the reflected
Room in my windows; I look in the mirror at night
And see two rooms, the first where left is right
And the second, beyond the reflected window, corrected
But there I am standing back to my back. The standard

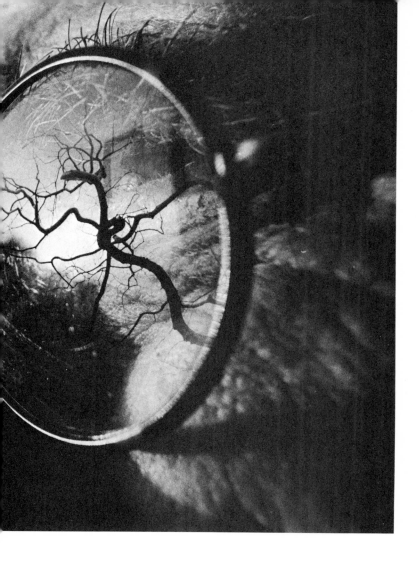

Lamp comes thrice in my mirror, twice in my window,
The fire in the mirror lies two rooms away through the
    window,
The fire in the window lies one room away down the
    terrace,
My actual room stands sandwiched between confections
Of night and lights and glass and in both directions

I can see beyond and through the reflections the street lamps
At home outdoors where my indoors rooms lie stranded,
Where a taxi perhaps will drive in through the bookcase
Whose books are not for reading and past the fire
Which gives no warmth and pull up by my desk
At which I cannot write since I am not lefthanded.

LOUIS MACNEICE

Mushrooms

Overnight, very
Whitely, discreetly,
Very quietly

Our toes, our noses
Take hold on the loam,
 Acquire the air.

Nobody sees us,
Stops us, betrays us;
The small grains make room.

Soft fists insist on
Heaving the needles,
The leafy bedding,

Even the paving.
Our hammers, our rams,
Earless and eyeless,

Perfectly voiceless,
Widen the crannies,
Shoulder through holes. We

Diet on water,
On crumbs of shadow,
Bland-mannered, asking

Little or nothing.
So many of us!
So many of us!

We are shelves, we are
Tables, we are meek,
We are edible,

Nudgers and shovers
In spite of ourselves.
Our kind multiplies:

We shall by morning
Inherit the earth.
Our foot's in the door.

SYLVIA PLATH

Pebble

The pebble
is a perfect creature

equal to itself
mindful of its limits

filled exactly
with a pebbly meaning

with a scent which does not remind one of anything
does not frighten anything away does not arouse desire

its ardour and coldness
are just and full of dignity

I feel a heavy remorse
when I hold it in my hand
and its noble body
is permeated by false warmth

— Pebbles cannot be tamed
to the end they will look at us
with a calm and very clear eye.

Z. HERBERT
(*Trans. C. Milosz and P. Dale Scott*)

Acquainted with the Night

I have been one acquainted with the night.
I have walked out in rain – and back in rain.
I have outwalked the furthest city light.

I have looked down the saddest city lane.
I have passed by the watchman on his beat
And dropped my eyes, unwilling to explain.

I have stood still and stopped the sound of feet
When far away an interrupted cry
Came over houses from another street,

But not to call me back or say goodbye;
And further still at an unearthly height,
One luminary clock against the sky
Proclaimed the time was neither wrong nor right.
I have been one acquainted with the night.

ROBERT FROST

52

Full Moon and Little Frieda

A cool small evening shrunk to a dog bark and the clank
    of a bucket –

And you listening.
A spider's web, tense for the dew's touch.
A pail lifted, still and brimming – mirror
To tempt a first star to a tremor.

Cows are going home in the lane there, looping the
    hedges with their warm wreaths of breath –
A dark river of blood, many boulders,
Balancing unspilled milk.

'Moon!' you cry suddenly, 'Moon! Moon!'

The moon has stepped back like an artist gazing amazed
    at a work
That points at him amazed.

TED HUGHES

Bare almond-trees

Wet almond-trees, in the rain,
Like iron sticking grimly out of the earth;
Black almond trunks, in the rain,
Like iron implements twisted, hideous, out of the earth,
Out of the deep, soft fledge of Sicilian winter-green,
Earth-grass uneatable,
Almond trunks curving blackly, iron-dark, climbing the
    slopes.

Almond-tree, beneath the terrace rail,
Black, rusted, iron trunk,
You have welded your thin stems finer,
Like steel, like sensitive steel in the air,
Grey, lavender, sensitive steel, curving thinly and brittly up
    in a parabola.

What are you doing in the December rain?
Have you a strange electric sensitiveness in your steel tips?
Do you feel the air for electric influences
Like some strange magnetic apparatus?
Do you take in messages, in some strange code,
From heaven's wolfish, wandering electricity, that prowls so
    constantly round Etna?
Do you take the whisper of sulphur from the air?
Do you hear the chemical accents of the sun?
Do you telephone the roar of the waters over the earth?
And from all this, do you make calculations?

Sicily, December's Sicily in a mass of rain
With iron branching blackly, rusted like old, twisted
    implements
And brandishing and stooping over earth's wintry fledge,
    climbing the slopes
Of uneatable soft green!

D. H. LAWRENCE

The Motion of the Earth

A day with sky so wide,
So stripped of cloud, so scrubbed, so vacuumed free
Of dust, that you can see
The earth-line as a curve, can watch the blue
Wrap over the edge, looping round and under,

Making you wonder
Whether the dark has anywhere left to hide.
But the world is slipping away; the polished sky
Gives nothing to grip on; clicked from the knuckle
The marble rolls along the gutter of time –
Earth, star and galaxy
Shifting their place in space.
Noon, sunset, clouds, the equably varying weather,
The diffused light, the illusion of blue,
Conceal each hour a different constellation.
All things are new
Over the sun, but we,
Our eyes on our shoes, go staring
At the asphalt, the gravel, the grass at the roadside, the door-
step, the doodles of snails, the crochet of mortar and lime,
Seeking the seeming familiar, though every stride
Takes us a thousand miles from where we were before.

NORMAN NICHOLSON

In The Microscope

Here too are dreaming landscapes,
lunar, derelict.
Here too are the masses
tillers of the soil.
And cells, fighters
who lay down their lives
for a song.

Here too are cemeteries,
fame and snow.
And I hear murmuring,
the revolt of immense estates.

MIROSLAV HOLUB
(*Trans. I. Milner and G. Theiner*)

55

Creative Writing

1 If you attempted to write haiku poetry following our suggestions on p. 5 you will be familiar with the syllable pattern and will have had experience of creating simple word-pictures. You may find it helpful now to think about this advice from one of Japan's greatest haiku poets, Shiki. After advising all writers of haiku to be, above all, natural and direct, he has this to say:

> *Remember perspective. Large things are large, but small things are also large if seen close up....*
> *Keep the words tight; put in nothing useless.*
> *Cut down as much as possible on adverbs and verbs.*
> *Use both imaginary pictures and real ones, but prefer the real ones.** *

You may want to discuss with your teacher this attitude to writing haiku.

Perhaps you could put one or two of Shiki's ideas into practice. Can you write a haiku where you do *remember perspective*? Or you may be able to write one in which you try to create a *real picture* which captures the uniqueness of a natural object – an outcrop of rocks, poplars or willow-trees, a butterfly, a cave, woods after a snowstorm, a field of corn or barley, a violent rainstorm. If you choose the last idea, Hokusai's picture of *Storm at Shono* on pp. 36–37 may suggest the atmosphere.

2 Write a sequel to D. H. Lawrence's poem *The Optimist* on p. 45. Call your poem *The Pessimist*.

3 Our ideas about big, complicated issues can often be defined quite sharply in terms of word-pictures.

Boys of your own age defined Death as
'beyond the night without your father'
and Fear as
'a very dark room with very white curtains'.

Perhaps you could attempt your own definitions of some of the following: Time, Beginning, Insincerity, Evil, Fear, Death, Hunger, Love, Loneliness, Wisdom, Happiness.

---

*From *An Introduction to Haiku* by H. G. Henderson (Doubleday Anchor) p. 161.

4 In Sylvia Plath's poem *Mushrooms* (p. 50) and Z. Herbert's poem *Pebble* (p. 51) non-human things seem to be endowed with a life of their own. Could you write a poem about the same sort of subject and imagine it "living" in this way? These suggestions may help: shells, balloons, fireworks, a piece of wood or coal, bones, a telegraph pole, a brick, moss, rust, mould, toadstools, tree roots, brambles, a marsh.

5 On pages 45 to 48 there are a number of poems about reflections in lakes, ponds, windows and mirrors which may give you an idea for a poem. The photograph on pp. 48–49 may help you.

Reflections in water often produce strange effects because things seen at different levels merge into each other. If you look down from a bridge into slow-moving water you will see objects on the surface – floating litter, water-flies, oil slicks; then perhaps, the reflection of yourself and your surroundings. Next, you may pick out sediment, weed, perhaps fish – things moving in the water; and, at the deepest level, perhaps you can make out the stones, tin-cans and other debris on the bottom.

Whichever type of reflection you choose to write about be aware of different pictures at different levels and remember the strange way in which your eyes do not seem able to keep these pictures separate.

PEOPLE

The Diviner

Cut from the green hedge a forked hazel stick
That he held tight by the arms of the V:
Circling the terrain, hunting the pluck
Of water, nervous, but professionally

Unfussed. The pluck came sharp as a sting.
The rod jerked down with precise convulsions,
Spring water suddenly broadcasting
Through a green aerial its secret stations.

The bystanders would ask to have a try.
He handed them the rod without a word.
It lay dead in their grasp till nonchalantly
He gripped expectant wrists. The hazel stirred.

SEAMUS HEANEY

The Equilibrist

The taut path of air
Flickers between his feet
That he poises on pin
Points: he dips a long
Leg deep into space,
He rides astride
The saddle of light
Wire and leaps right

58

Out of himself on
To nothing, nimble perch,
Fluttering sharp
Fans or hoisting a tight
Parasol, the odd
Wings of his unequal hands
As he dallies on springs
Of space from one
Place to another, minces
High on the prancing wire
That curvets like deep
Water whose high
Sea's single wave
He playfully wanders and –
        –but this, too,
Is meditated, and
It is we who, caught
Off our balance, willingly
Tripped
      and
         fell.
        JAMES KIRKUP

Gallows Bird

He stares at his toes
Where ice makes him nails

It rolls down his thighs
The wind fills his nose

And the dust of his thought
Licks its vault

Bald, eyeless, caught,
He grins at his toes
Though ice makes him nails.
Is this the gross cutthroat?
With nods and smiles?

A vine catches his toes,
Nettles reach to his knees,
Honey slips from his teeth,
His head brims with bees,
Wax pads his eyes,
Rocking at ease
He hums to himself,
And the moss all the while
Is closing his eyes,
Is bearding his smile.

PETER REDGROVE

African Beggar

Sprawled in the dust outside the Syrian store,
a target for small children, dogs and flies,
a heap of verminous rags and matted hair,
he watches us with cunning, reptile eyes,
his noseless, smallpoxed face creased in a sneer.

Sometimes he shows his yellow stumps of teeth
and whines for alms, perceiving that we bear
the curse of pity; a grotesque mask of death,
with hands like claws about his begging-bowl.

But often he is lying all alone
within the shadow of a crumbling wall,
lost in the trackless jungle of his pain,
clutching the pitiless red earth in vain
and whimpering like a stricken animal.

RAYMOND TONG

Blind

His headstrong thoughts that once in eager strife
Leapt sure from eye to brain and back to eye,
Weaving unconscious tapestries of life,
Are now thrust inward, dungeoned from the sky.
   And he who has watched his world and loved it all,
   Starless and old and blind, a sight for pity,
   With feeble steps and fingers on the wall,
   Gropes with his staff along the rumbling city.

SIEGFRIED SASSOON

Gunpowder Plot

For days these curious cardboard buds have lain
In brightly coloured boxes. Soon the night
Will come. We pray there'll be no sullen rain
To make these magic orchids flame less bright.

Now in the garden's darkness they begin
To flower: the frenzied whizz of Catherine-wheel
Puts forth its fiery petals and the thin
Rocket soars to burst upon the steel

Bulwark of a cloud. And then the guy,
Absurdly human phoenix, is again
Gulped by greedy flames: the harvest sky
Is flecked with threshed and glittering golden grain.

'Uncle! A cannon! Watch me as I light it!'
The women helter-skelter, squealing high,
Retreat; the paper fuse is quickly lit,
A cat-like hiss, and spit of fire, a sly

Falter, then the air is shocked with blast.
The cannon bangs and in my nostrils drifts
A bitter scent that brings the lurking past
Lurching to my side. The present shifts,

Allows a ten-year memory to walk
Unhindered now; and so I'm forced to hear
The banshee howl of mortar and the talk
Of men who died, am forced to taste my fear.

I listen for a moment to the guns,
The torn earth's grunts, recalling how I prayed.
The past retreats. I hear a corpse's sons –
'Who's scared of bangers!' 'Uncle! John's afraid!'
VERNON SCANNELL

Two Travellers

One of us in the compartment stares
Out of his window the whole day long
With attentive mien, as if he knows
There is hid in the journeying scene a song
To recall or compose
From snatches of vision, hints of vanishing airs.

He'll mark the couched hares
In grass whereover the lapwing reel and twist:
He notes how the shockheaded sunflowers climb
Like boys on the wire by the railway line;
And for him those morning rivers are love-in-a-mist,
And the chimneystacks prayers.

The other is plainly a man of affairs,
A seasoned commuter. His looks assert,
As he opens his briefcase intent on perusing
Facts and figures, he'd never divert
With profitless musing
The longest journey, or notice the dress it wears.

Little he cares
For the coloured drift of his passage: no, not a thing
Values in all that is hurrying past,
Though dimly he senses from first to last
How flaps and waves the smoke of his travelling
At the window-squares.

One is preoccupied, one just stares,
While the whale-ribbed terminus nears apace
Where passengers all must change, and under
Its arch triumphal quickly disperse.
So you may wonder,
Watching these two whom the train indifferently bears,
What each of them shares
With his fellow-traveller, and which is making the best of it,
And whether this or the other one
Will be justified when the journey's done,
And if either may carry on some reward or regret for it
Whither he fares.

C. DAY LEWIS

On Andrew Turner

In se'enteen hunder 'n forty-nine,
The deil gat stuff to mak a swine,
   An' coost it in a corner;
But wilily he chang'd his plan,
An' shap'd it something like a man,
   An' ca'd it Andrew Turner.
               ROBERT BURNS

Address to Toothache

My curse upon your venom'd stang,
That shoots my tortur'd gooms alang,
An' thro' my lug gies monie a twang,
      Wi' gnawing vengeance,
Tearing my nerves wi' bitter pang,
      Like racking engines!

A' down me beard the slavers trickle,
I throw the wee stools o'er the mickle,
While round the fire the giglets keckle[1],   [1] girls giggle
      To see me loup[2],   [2] leap
An', raving mad, I wish a heckle[3]   [3] sharp pin
      Were i' their doup[4]!   [4] backside

When fevers burn, or agues freeze us,
Rheumatics gnaw, or colics squeeze us,
Our neibor's sympathy may ease us,
      Wi' pitying moan;
But thee! – thou hell o' a' diseases –
      They mock our groan.

Of a' the numerous human dools,
Ill hairsts[5], daft bargains, cutty stools[6] [5]harvests [6]stools of
Or worthy frien's rak'd i' the mools[7] – [7]dust repentance
     Sad sight to see!
The tricks o' knaves, or fash o' fools,
     Thou bear'st the gree!

Where'er that place be priests ca' hell,
Where a' the tones o' misery yell,
An' ranked plagues their numbers tell,
     In dreadfu' raw,
Thou, TOOTHACHE, surely bear'st the bell,
     Amang them a'!

O thou grim, mischief-making chiel,
That gars the notes o' discord squeel,
Till daft mankind aft dance a reel
     In gore, a shoe-thick,
Gie a' the faces o' SCOTLAND'S weal
     A townmond's[8] toothache! [8]a year-long
                ROBERT BURNS

Wednesbury Cocking

At Wednesbury there was a cocking,
   A match between Newton and Scroggins;
The colliers and nailers left work,
   And all to old Spittle's went jogging.
To see this noble sport,
   Many noblemen resorted;
And though they'd but little money,
   Yet that little they freely sported.

There was Jeffery and Colborn from Hampton,
    And Dusty from Bilston was there;
Plummery he came from Darlaston,
    And he was as rude as a bear.
There was old Will from Walsall,
    And Smacker from Westbromich come;
Blind Robin he come from Rowley,
    And staggering he went home.

Ralph Moody came hobbling along,
    As though he some cripple were mocking,
To join in the blackguard throng,
    That met at Wednesbury cocking.
He borrowed a trifle of Doll,
    To back old Taverner's grey;
He laid fourpence-halfpenny to fourpence,
    He lost and went broken away.

But soon he returned to the pit,
    For he'd borrowed a trifle more money,
And ventured another large bet,
    Along with blobbermouth Coney.
When Coney demanded his money,
    As is common on such occasions,
He cried, 'Rot thee, if thee don't hold thy rattle,
    I'll pay thee as Paul payed the Ephesians.'

The morning's sport being over,
    Old Spittle a dinner proclaimed,
Each man he should dine for a groat,
    If he grumbled he ought to be maimed,
For there was plenty of beef,
    But Spittle he swore by his troth,
That never a man he should dine
    Till he'd ate his noggin of broth.

The beef it was old and tough,
  Off a bull that was baited to death,
Barney Hyde got a lump in his throat,
  That had like to have stopped his breath,
The company all fell into confusion,
  At seeing poor Barney Hyde choke;
So they took him into the kitchen,
  And held him over the smoke.

They held him so close to the fire,
  He frizzled just like a beef-steak,
Then they threw him down on the floor,
  Which had like to have broken his neck.
One gave him a kick in the stomach,
  Another a clout on the brow,
His wife said, 'Throw him into the stable,
  And he'll be better just now.'

Then they all returned to the pit,
  And the fighting went forward again;
Six battles were fought on each side,
  And the next was to décide the main.
For they were two famous cocks
  As ever this country bred,
Scroggin's a dark winged black,
  And Newton's a shift winged red.

The conflict was hard on both sides,
  Till Brassy's black winged was choked;
The colliers were tarnationly vexed,
  And the nailers were sorely provoked.
Peter Stevens he swore a great oath,
  That Scroggins had played his cock foul;
Scroggins gave him a kick on the head,
  And cried, 'Yea, God damn thy soul!'

The company then fell in discord,
  A bold, bold fight did ensue;
Kick, bludgeon and bite was the word,
  Till the Walsall men all were subdued.
Ralph Moody bit off a man's nose,
  And wished that he could have him slain,
So they trampled both cocks to death,
  And they made a draw of the main.

The cock-pit was near to the church,
  An ornament unto the town;
On one side an old coal pit,
  The other well gorsed around.
Peter Hadley peeped through the gorse,
  In order to see them all fight;
Spittle jobbed out his eye with a fork,
  And said, 'Rot thee, it served thee right.'

Some people may think this strange,
  Who Wednesbury never knew;
But those who have ever been there,
  Won't have the least doubt it is true;
For they are so savage by nature,
  And guilty of deeds the most shocking;
Jack Baker he whacked his own father,
  And thus ended Wednesbury cocking.

                                    ANON

Her Husband

Comes home dull with coal-dust deliberately
To grime the sink and foul towels and let her
Learn with scrubbing brush and scrubbing board
The stubborn character of money.

And let her learn through what kind of dust
He has earned his thirst and the right to quench it
And what sweat he has exchanged for his money
And the blood-count of money. He'll humble her

With new light on her obligations.
The fried, woody chips, kept warm two hours in the oven,
Are only part of her answer.
Hearing the rest, he slams them to the fire-back

And is away round the house-end singing
'Come back to Sorrento' in a voice
Of resounding corrugated iron.
Her back has bunched into a hump as an insult . . .

For they will have their rights.
Their jurors are to be assembled
From the little crumbs of soot. Their brief
Goes straight up to heaven and nothing more is heard of it.

TED HUGHES

Farm Child

Look at this village boy, his head is stuffed
    With all the nests he knows, his pockets with flowers,
    Snail-shells and bits of glass, the fruit of hours
Spent in the fields by thorn and thistle tuft.

Look at his eyes, see the harebell hiding there;
    Mark how the sun has freckled his smooth face
Like a finch's egg under that bush of hair
    That dares the wind, and in the mixen[1] now   [1]dung-hill
    Notice his poise; from such unconscious grace
    Earth breeds and beckons to the stubborn plough.

R. S. THOMAS

A Moment of Respect

Two things I remember about my grandfather:
his threadbare trousers, and the way he adjusted
his half-hunter watch two minutes every day.

When I asked him why he needed to know the time
   so
exactly, he said a business man could lose a fortune
by being two minutes late for an appointment.

When he died he left two meerschaum pipes
and a golden sovereign on a chain. Somebody
threw the meerschaum pipes away, and
there was an argument about the sovereign.

On the day of his burial the church clock chimed
as he was lowered down into the clay, and all
the family advanced their watches by two minutes.

EDWIN BROCK

Redemption

Having been tenant long to a rich Lord
  Not thriving, I resolved to be bold,
  And make a suit unto him, to afford
A new small-rented lease, and cancell th'old.
In heaven at his manour I him sought:
  They told me there, that he was lately gone
  About some land, which he had dearly bought
Long since on earth, to take possession.
I straight return'd, and knowing his great birth,
  Sought him accordingly in great resorts;
  In cities, theatres, gardens, parks, and courts:

72

At length I heard a ragged noise and mirth
Of theeves and murderers: there I him espied,
Who straight, *Your suit is granted*, said, and died.
                                                    GEORGE HERBERT

The Oxen

Christmas Eve, and twelve of the clock,
    'Now they are all on their knees,'
An elder said as we sat in a flock
    By the embers in hearthside ease.

We pictured the meek mild creatures where
    They dwelt in their strawy pen,
Nor did it occur to one of us there
    To doubt they were kneeling then.

So fair a fancy few would weave
    In these years! Yet I feel,
If someone said on Christmas Eve,
    'Come; see the oxen kneel

'In the lonely barton by yonder comb
    Our childhood used to know,'
I should go with him in the gloom,
    Hoping it might be so.
                                                    THOMAS HARDY

A Poison Tree

I was angry with my friend:
I told my wrath, my wrath did end.
I was angry with my foe:
I told it not, my wrath did grow.

And I water'd it in fears,
Night and morning with my tears;
And I sunnéd it with smiles,
And with soft deceitful wiles.

And it grew both day and night,
Till it bore an apple bright;
And my foe beheld it shine,
And he knew that it was mine,

And into my garden stole
When the night had veil'd the pole:
In the morning glad I see
My foe outstretch'd beneath the tree.

WILLIAM BLAKE

Love without Hope

Love without hope, as when the young bird-catcher
Swept off his tall hat to the Squire's own daughter,
So let the imprisoned larks escape and fly
Singing about her head, as she rode by.

ROBERT GRAVES

nobody loses all the time

nobody loses all the time

i had an uncle named
Sol who was a born failure and
nearly everybody said he should have gone
into vaudeville perhaps because my Uncle Sol could
sing McCann He Was A Diver on Xmas Eve like Hell
    Itself which
may or may not account for the fact that my Uncle

Sol indulged in that possibly most inexcusable
of all to use a highfalootin phrase
luxuries that is or to
wit farming and be
it needlessly
added

my Uncle Sol's farm
failed because the chickens
ate the vegetables so
my Uncle Sol had a
chicken farm till the
skunks ate the chickens when

my Uncle Sol
had a skunk farm but
the skunks caught cold and
died and so
my Uncle Sol imitated the
skunks in a subtle manner

or by drowning himself in the watertank
but somebody who'd given my Uncle Sol a Victor
Victrola and records while he lived presented to
him upon the auspicious occasion of his decease a
scrumptious not to mention splendiferous funeral with
tall boys in black gloves and flowers and everything and

i remember we all cried like the Missouri
when my Uncle Sol's coffin lurched because
somebody pressed a button
(and down went
my Uncle
Sol

and started a worm farm)

E. E. CUMMINGS

Facts of Death

The play is over:
You can die now.
G. P. WALLEY

Epitaph on Charles the Second

Here lies our Sovereign Lord the King,
   Whose word no man relies on,
Who never said a foolish thing,
   Nor ever did a wise one.
JOHN WILMOT

Epitaph

The poem in the rock and
The poem in the mind
Are not one.
It was in dying
I tried to make them so.
R. S. THOMAS

Epitaph on a Pessimist

I'm Smith of Stoke, aged sixty-odd,
   I've lived without a dame
From youth-time on; and would to God
   My dad had done the same.
THOMAS HARDY
(*from the French and Greek*)

On the Death of
Sir A. Morton's Wife

He first deceased – she, for a little, tried
To live without him, liked it not and died.
HENRY WOTTON

Lather As You Go

Beneath this slab
John Brown is stowed.
He watched the ads.,
And not the road.
OGDEN NASH

Matthew Bird

I, the Reverend Matthew Bird,
Preacher of God's Holy Word,
Taking leave of aisle and pew,
Go to find how much is true.
L. A. G. STRONG

Creative Writing

1 A number of the poems in this section are about people whose characters or occupations are unusual. Is there anyone who stands out in your own mind in this way? Someone, perhaps, who is eccentric or frightening. What are the things which distinguish this person? Examine your feelings about your subject carefully before you try to write your poem.

2 Do you still keep any of your old, childhood toys? Very often there is one particular toy which people become attached to and which has special associations and memories connected with it: a teddy-bear, an old bicycle, a toy pistol, a dolls' house, a rocking-horse. . . .

    Perhaps you could write about your own special toy, the memories that it brings back and the feelings that you have about it now.

3 On pp. 77 and 78 there are a number of epitaphs, some serious, some humorous, some expressing thoughts about the nature of life and death. You may like to write one or two epitaphs of your own. Keep them brief. If you want to be witty, rhymes may help; if you want to be solemn, rhymes are perhaps best avoided and you may need to write at greater length.

    Do not think that the more generalised *Facts of Death* (p. 77) is beyond you: a boy of your own age wrote it.

4 The photograph on p. 10 may remind you of holidays at the seaside when you have walked alone along the shore. Try to put yourself in the place of the person in the picture. What do you imagine his thoughts might be? What does he notice around him? Can you find any phrases or comparisons for the patterns in the sand? his shadow? the pools? the sunlight on the beach? What details do you notice? What might you be aware of through your other senses? Can you put some of these ideas into a poem?

5 The photograph of the boy on bonfire night on p. 62 was taken by someone of your own age. It may remind you of the atmosphere of November the fifth. Look at the picture carefully and imagine you are the boy holding the fireworks. Jot down quickly phrases and comparisons along the following lines:

    What do you see? Look at the circular trail of the sparklers – there is plenty of scope for comparison here.

79

What do you hear?
What do you smell as the firework steadily burns down?
What do the fireworks feel like in your hands?
Try to write a poem from your notes.

6 The portrait on p. 70 shows a Lancashire coal-miner. What details do you notice about his appearance? Look carefully at his face, particularly at the eyes and the mouth. What do you notice about his hand? his clothes? Does his appearance suggest his character to you or the sort of demands made upon him by his job? You may be able to write about him.

PLACES

The Pond

With nets and kitchen sieves they raid the pond,
Chasing the minnows into bursts of mud,
Scooping and chopping, raking up frond after frond
Of swollen weed after a week of flood.

Thirty or forty minnows bob and flash
In every jam-jar hoarded on the edge,
While the shrill children with each ill-aimed splash
Haul out another dozen as they dredge.

Choked to its banks, the pond spills out its store
Of frantic life. Nothing can drain it dry
Of what it breeds: it breeds so effortlessly
Theft seems to leave it richer than before.

The nostrils snuff its rank bouquet – how warm,
How lavish, foul, and indiscriminate, fat
With insolent appetite and thirst, so that
The stomach almost heaves to see it swarm.

But trapped in glass the minnows flail and fall,
Sink, with upended bellies showing white.
After an hour I look and see that all
But four or five have died. The greenish light

Ripples to stillness, while the children bend
To spoon the corpses out, matter-of-fact,
Absorbed: as if creation's prodigal act
Shrank to this empty jam-jar in the end.

ANTHONY THWAITE

81

The Beach

Louder than gulls the little children scream
Whom fathers haul into the jovial foam;
But others fearlessly rush in, breast high,
Laughing the salty water from their mouths –
Heroes of the nursery.

The horny boatman, who has seen whales
And flying fishes, who has sailed as far
As Demerara and the Ivory Coast,
Will warn them, when they crowd to hear his tales,
That every ocean smells alike of tar.

ROBERT GRAVES

Going Away and Returning

The best of going away is the going –
That inland sea view
Glimpsed through gaps in a traffic queue;
White mosques on stilts of a pier striding
Towards empty horizons blue with dreaming.

Jolted, we arrive
At Bella Vista gleaming
Gull-grey on a grey parade
Where tired waves at high-tide flap-
Flop, slopping on grey stones.

Later the swept shore is sad
With deck-chair sleepers, paddling children, mad
Mothers grabbing their infants from the sea,
Couples linked by hoarse transistors,
Picnic-papers,
Castles built to be washed away,
And shells,
Scoured, gathered, taken home
To a blind house that smells
Of lack and damp.

Return is dead flowers
In the same vase;
That letter unanswered on the fridge;
Floor unswept;
Clock stopped; range
Cold – the worst of coming back is the kept
Secret of a locked house,
Ourselves on the outside, strange.

PHOEBE HESKETH

A House in Summer

In the dusk of garden fagged by the electric day,
Pale washing hung beyond the blackening roses
Shifts like restless visitors who cannot get away.
The blinding sun is clenched, as evening discomposes,
In dunderheaded clouds, that squeeze it out of sight.
Great trees are staggered by the merest breath of night.

All doors are open in the choking house,
And no one seems to know where anyone has gone:
All are at home, but absent; in, but out.
A person leans in a twilight corner like a gun,
Lighting his face with the last rays from a book
Whose leaves never stir, though he gives them look after
   look.

At an open window, a tree rustles, curiously close, its wood
Full of exhausted patience, patient still.
The window seems to take in much more than it should –
An entire garden, the lake beyond, a dog over a hill:
They are all inside the open house, like the air
Moved in from the afternoon, left hanging round the stair.

In the bedrooms, twilight cannot quite extinguish
The blank abandon of beds unmade by heat.
The morning's thrown-back coverings bloom and languish
Like knocked-out lovers under the ceiling's even sheet.
The attics throb like ovens and their stone tiles tick.
Baked books are warm still, their floury pages thick.

A door closes. Another. A window left open is no longer
   wide.
A looking-glass is blighted with its own vain repetitions:
Its dusty coolness draws the lost inhabitants inside.
– Faces dark with summer, they drift like apparitions,
Bringing each other the last of day, the first of night
In a wide room suddenly shuttered by unnatural light.

JAMES KIRKUP

Autobiographical Note

Beeston, the place, near Nottingham;
We lived there for three years or so.
Each Saturday at two o'clock
We queued up for the matinee,
All the kids for streets around
With snotty noses, giant caps,
Cut down coats and heavy boots,
The natural enemies of cops
And schoolteachers. Profane and hoarse
We scrambled, yelled and fought until
The Picture Palace opened up
And then, like Hamelin children, forced
Our bony way into the Hall.
That much is easy to recall;
Also the reek of chewing-gum,
Gob-stoppers and liquorice,
But of the flickering myths themselves
Not much remains. The hero was
A milky, wide-brimmed hat, a shape
Astride the arched white stallion.
The villain's horse and hat were black.
Disbelief did not exist
And laundered virtue always won
With quicker gun and harder fist
And all of us applauded it.
Yet I remember moments when
In solitude I'd find myself
Brooding on the sooty man,
The bristling villain,.who could move
Imagination in a way
The well-shaved hero never could,
And even warm the nervous heart
With something oddly close to love.

VERNON SCANNELL

Approach to a City

Getting through with the world –
I never tire of the mystery
of these streets: the three baskets
of dried flowers in the high

bar-room window, the gulls wheeling
above the factory, the dirty
snow – the humility of the snow that
silvers everything and is

trampled and lined with use – yet
falls again, the silent birds
on the still wires of the sky, the blur
of wings as they take off

together. The flags in the heavy
air move against a leaden
ground – the snow
pencilled with the stubble of old

weeds: I never tire of these sights
but refresh myself there
always for there is small holiness
to be found in braver things.

WILLIAM CARLOS WILLIAMS

Leaving Town

It was impossible to leave the town.
Bumping across a maze of obsolete rails
Three times we reached the gasworks and reversed.
We could not get away from the canal;
Dead cats, dead hopes, in those grey deeps immersed,
Over our efforts breathed a spectral prayer.
The cattle-market and the gospel-hall
Returned like fictions of our own despair,
And like Hesperides the suburbs seemed,

Shining far off towards the guiltless fields.
We finished in a little cul-de-sac
Where on the pavement sat a ragged girl
Mourning beside a jug-and-bottle entrance.
Once more we turned the car and started back.

JAMES REEVES

Slough

Come, friendly bombs, and fall on Slough
It isn't fit for humans now,
There isn't grass to graze a cow
    Swarm over, Death!

Come, bombs, and blow to smithereens
Those air-conditioned, bright canteens,
Tinned fruit, tinned meat, tinned milk, tinned beans
    Tinned minds, tinned breath.

Mess up the mess they call a town –
A house for ninety-seven down
And once a week a half-a-crown
    For twenty years.

And get that man with double chin
Who'll always cheat and always win,
Who washes his repulsive skin
    In women's tears.

And smash his desk of polished oak
And smash his hands so used to stroke
And stop his boring dirty joke
    And make him yell.

But spare the bald young clerks who add
The profits of the stinking cad;
It's not their fault that they are mad,
   They've tasted Hell.

It's not their fault they do not know
The birdsong from the radio,
It's not their fault they often go
   To Maidenhead

And talk of sports and makes of cars
In various bogus Tudor bars
And daren't look up and see the stars
   But belch instead.

In labour-saving homes, with care
Their wives frizz out peroxide hair
And dry it in synthetic air
   And paint their nails.

Come, friendly bombs, and fall on Slough
To get it ready for the plough.
The cabbages are coming now:
   The earth exhales.

JOHN BETJEMAN

Earthquake

An old man's flamingo-coloured kite
Twitches higher over tiled roofs.
Idly gazing through the metal gauze
That nets the winter sun beyond my sliding windows,
I notice that all the telegraph poles along the lane
Are waggling convulsively, and the wires
Bounce like skipping-ropes round flustered birds.
The earth creeps under the floor. A cherry tree
Agitates itself outside, but it is no wind
That makes the long bamboo palisade
Begin to undulate down all its length.

The clock stammers and stops. There is a queer racket,
Like someone rapping on the wooden walls,
Then through the ceiling's falling flakes I see
The brass handles on a high chest of drawers
Dithering and dancing in a brisk distraction.
The lamp swings like a headache, and the whole house
Rotates slightly on grinding rollers.
Smoothly, like a spoilt child putting out a tongue,
A drawer shoots half-out, and quietly glides back again,
Closed with a snap of teeth, a sharper click
Than such a casual grimace prepared me for.

The stove-pipe's awkward elbow
Twangles its three supporting wires. Doors
Slam, fly open: my quiet maid erupts from
Nowhere, blushing furiously, yet smiling wildly
As if to explain, excuse, console and warn.
Together, like lost children in a fairy-tale
Who escape from an enchanter's evil cottage,
We rush out into the slightly unbalanced garden. A pole
Vibrates still like a plucked bass string,
But the ground no longer squirms beneath our feet,
And the trees are composing themselves, have birds again.

In the spooky quiet, a 'plane drones
Like a metal top, and though the sound
Gives a sense of disaster averted,
And is even oddly re-assuring, as
The pulse of confident engines,
Throbbing high above an electric storm, can comfort,
We feel that somewhere out of sight
Something has done its worst. Meanwhile,
The house tries to look as if nothing had happened,
And over the roof's subtle curves
Lets the flamingo-coloured kite fly undisturbed.

JAMES KIRKUP

Depopulation of the Hills

Leave it, leave it – the hole under the door
Was a mouth through which the rough wind spoke
Even more sharply; the dank hand
Of age was busy on the walls
Scrawling in blurred characters
Messages of hate and fear.

Leave it, leave it – the cold rain began
At summer end – there is no road
Over the bog, and winter comes
With mud above the axletree.

Leave it, leave it – the rain dripped
Day and night from the patched roof
Sagging beneath its load of sky.

Did the earth help them, time befriend
These last survivors? Did the spring grass
Heal winter's ravages? The grass
Wrecked them in its draughty tides,
Grew from the chimney-stack like smoke,
Burned its way through the weak timbers.
That was nature's jest, the sides
Of the old hulk cracked, but not with mirth.

R. S. THOMAS

Wuthering Heights

The horizons ring me like faggots,
Tilted and disparate, and always unstable.
Touched by a match, they might warm me,
And their fine lines singe
The air to orange
Before the distances they pin evaporate,
Weighting the pale sky with a solider colour.
But they only dissolve and dissolve
Like a series of promises, as I step forward.

There is no life higher than the grasstops
Or the hearts of sheep, and the wind
Pours by like destiny, bending
Everything in one direction.
I can feel it trying
To funnel my heat away.
If I pay the roots of heather
Too close attention, they will invite me
To whiten my bones among them.

94

The sheep know where they are,
Browsing in their dirty wool-clouds,
Grey as the weather,
The black slots of their pupils take me in.
It is like being mailed into space,
A thin silly message.
They stand about in grandmotherly disguise,
All wig curls and yellow teeth
And hard, marbly baas.

I come to wheel ruts and water
Limpid as the solitudes
That flee through my fingers.
Hollow doorsteps go from grass to grass;
Lintel and sill have unhinged themselves.
Of people the air only
Remembers a few odd syllables.
It rehearses them moaningly:
Black stone, black stone.

The sky leans on me, me, the one upright
Among all horizontals.
The grass is beating its head distractedly.
It is too delicate
For a life in such company;
Darkness terrifies it.
Now, in valleys narrow
And black as purses, the house lights
Gleam like small change.

SYLVIA PLATH

Tea in a Space-Ship

In this world a tablecloth need not be laid
On any table, but is spread out anywhere
Upon the always equidistant and
Invisible legs of gravity's wild air.

The tea, which never would grow cold,
Gathers itself into a wet and steaming ball,
And hurls its liquid molecules at anybody's head,
Or dances, eternal bilboquet,
In and out of the suspended cups up-
Ended in the weightless hands
Of chronically nervous jerks
Who yet would never spill a drop,
Their mouths agape for passing cakes.

Lumps of sparkling sugar
Sling themselves out of their crystal bowl
With a disordered fountain's
Ornamental stops and starts.
The milk describes a permanent parabola
Girdled with satellites of spinning tarts.

The future lives with graciousness.
The hostess finds her problems eased,
For there is honey still for tea
And butter keeps the ceiling greased.

She will provide, of course,
No cake-forks, spoons or knives.
They are so sharp, so dangerously gadabout,
It is regarded as a social misdemeanour
To put them out.

JAMES KIRKUP

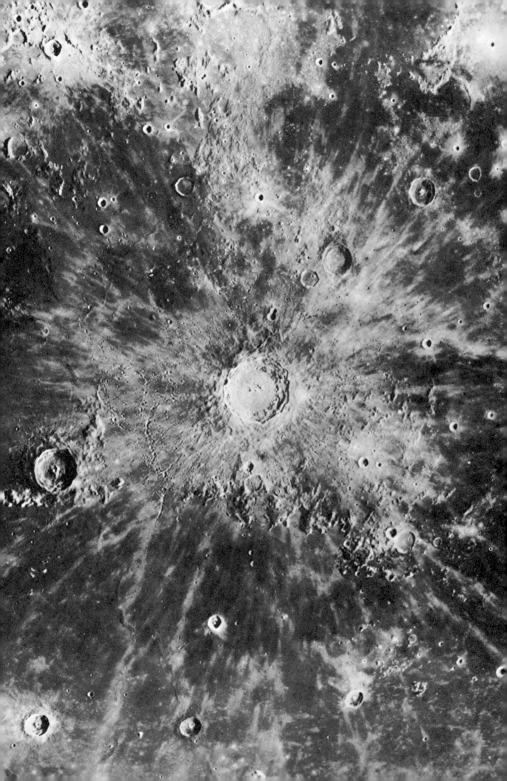

Creative Writing

1 The atmosphere of places seems to vary according to the time of day: the same road may take on quite a different character in the evening dusk from that which it had earlier in the day. Think of your own road at one of these times. What do you notice about the light? About shadows? Does the air feel different? If so, how do you become aware of this – through smells? through temperature? Is there any particular sound which you associate with either time of day? Are there any particular people about at these times?

   Night has its own special atmosphere. Most of you will have lain awake at some time aware of the sounds and shapes in the darkness about you.

   What sort of sounds do you notice?

   Can you think of any words or comparisons to describe the darkness?

   Usually you can make out some shapes. What do they remind you of? What are your feelings?

   Perhaps some light comes in from outside from the street-lights, the moon, or from car headlights. Can you find words or comparisons to describe its effect?

   You may be able to write a poem from one of these ideas.

2 Most of you will have seen a road accident, or at least the aftermath; some of you may even have been involved in one. Visualise the scene in your imagination. What details catch your eye?

   What does the bodywork look like? The windows . . . the wheels . . . the doors? Are any comparisons suggested?

   Are there any people on the scene? What are their reactions? What are *your* feelings?

   Try to capture the scene in a poem.

3 Attics and cellars are often strange and rarely visited parts of houses. Your own home may have them or you may have visited a house which has. Jot down quickly some of the things that you see there and try to capture the atmosphere of the place in a poem.

4 Look at the photograph of the moon's surface on p. 97. Write down quickly as many words, phrases and comparisons as you can to describe its appearance. When you have finished your

notes you may be able to use them as the basis for a poem entitled "Moon Landing" in which you imagine the last stages of a spacecraft's descent to the moon's surface. How does the appearance of the moon change as you get closer? It may help you to imagine yourself falling into the photograph.

5 William Carlos Williams' poem *Approach to a City* on p. 88 picks out a number of small but memorable details which he associates with an area he knows well. Look carefully at the details he records – some moving, others still; some for their colour, others for their shape. Perhaps you could do the same in describing a street which is familiar to you.

6 The three photographs on opp. 83, 87 and 89 each show very different scenes. Jot down phrases, comparisons and ideas about either the back-street, the cranes or the stalactites in the cave as they are suggested to you by the pictures. You may be able to write a poem from your notes.

SEASONS

Spring

To pass by a pondbrink
Trodden by horses
Where among the green horsetails
Even the hoofprints
Shiver with tadpoles
Comma'ed with offspring
And moist buds flick awake
On breeze-floundering sallows.

PETER REDGROVE

March

Awake to the cold light
of wet wind running
twigs in tremors. Walls
are naked. Twilights raw –
and when the sun taps steeples
their glistenings dwindle
upward . . .

March
slips along the ground
like a mouse under pussy
willows, a little hungry.

The vagrant ghost of winter,
is it this that keeps the chimney
busy still? For something still
nudges shingles and windows:

but waveringly, – this ghost,
this slate-eyed saintly wraith
of winter wanes
and knows its waning.

HART CRANE

May Day

The whole county apparently afloat:
Every road bridging or skirting water,
The land islanded, lough and burn
                              turned moat.

That bulrush at attention. I had to
Wade barefoot over spongy, ice-cold marsh
(No bottom, just water seeping through

The netted weed) to get near where it stood
Perennially dry among May blossoming,
Chalky, velvety, rooted in liquid.

The elements running to watercolour,
The skyline filled up to the very brim.
The globe was flooded inwardly, fuller

Than a melon, the rind not even solid
For remember, in a ditch, the
                              unstanched spring
Flushing itself all over the road.

SEAMUS HEANEY

July

... noon burns with its blistering breath
Around, and day dies still as death.
The busy noise of man and brute
Is on a sudden lost and mute;
Even the brook that leaps along
Seems weary of its bubbling song,
And, so soft its waters creep,
Tired silence sinks in sounder sleep.
The very flies forget to hum;
And, save the waggon rocking round,
The landscape sleeps without a sound.
The breeze is stopt, the lazy bough
Hath not a leaf that dances now;
The totter-grass upon the hill,
And spiders' threads, are standing still;
The feathers dropt from moor-hen's wing,
Which to the water's surface cling,
Are steadfast, and as heavy seem
As stones beneath them in the stream;
Hawkweed and groundsel's fanning downs
Unruffled keep their seedy crowns;
And in the oven-heated air,
Not one light thing is floating there,
Save that to the earnest eye,
The restless heat seems twittering by.

From *The Shepherd's Calendar*
JOHN CLARE

Blackberry-Picking

For Philip Hobsbaum

Late August, given heavy rain and sun
For a full week, the blackberries would ripen.
At first, just one, a glossy purple clot
Among others, red, green, hard as a knot.
You ate that first one and its flesh was sweet
Like thickened wine: summer's blood was in it
Leaving stains upon the tongue and lust for
Picking. Then red ones inked up and that hunger
Sent us out with milk-cans, pea-tins, jam-pots
Where briars scratched and wet grass bleached our boots.
Round hayfields, cornfields and potato-drills
We trekked and picked until the cans were full,
Until the tinkling bottom had been covered
With green ones, and on top big dark blobs burned
Like a plate of eyes. Our hands were peppered
With thorn pricks, our palms sticky as Bluebeard's.

We hoarded the fresh berries in the byre.
But when the bath was filled we found a fur,
A rat-grey fungus, glutting on our cache.
The juice was stinking too. Once off the bush
The fruit fermented, the sweet flesh would turn sour.
I always felt like crying. It wasn't fair
That all the lovely canfuls smelt of rot.
Each year I hoped they'd keep, knew they would not.

SEAMUS HEANEY

Season

Rust is ripeness, rust
And the wilted corn-plume;
Pollen is mating-time when swallows
Weave a dance
Of feathered arrows
Thread corn-stalks in winged
Streaks of light. And, we loved to hear
Spliced phrases of the wind, to hear
Rasps in the field, where corn leaves
Pierce like bamboo slivers.

Now, garnerers we,
Awaiting rust on tassels, draw
Long shadows from the dusk, wreathe
Dry thatch in woodsmoke. Laden stalks
Ride the germ's decay – we await
The promise of the rust.

WOLE SOYINKA

To Autumn

I

Season of mists and mellow fruitfulness,
  Close bosom-friend of the maturing sun;
Conspiring with him how to load and bless
  With fruit the vines that round the thatch-eaves run;
To bend with apples the moss'd cottage-trees,
  And fill all fruit with ripeness to the core;
    To swell the gourd, and plump the hazel shells
  With a sweet kernel; to set budding more,
And still more, later flowers for the bees,
Until they think warm days will never cease,
    For Summer has o'er-brimmed their clammy cells.

Who hath not seen thee oft amid thy store?
  Sometimes whoever seeks abroad may find
Thee sitting careless on a granary floor,
  Thy hair soft-lifted by the winnowing wind;
Or on a half-reaped furrow sound asleep,
  Drows'd with the fume of poppies, while thy hook
    Spares the next swath and all its twined flowers:
And sometimes like a gleaner thou dost keep
  Steady thy laden head across a brook;
  Or by a cyder-press, with patient look,
    Thou watchest the last oozings hours by hours.

III

Where are the songs of Spring? Ah, where are they?
  Think not of them, thou hast thy music too, –
While barred clouds bloom the soft-dying day,
  And touch the stubble-plains with rosy hue;
Then in a wailful choir the small gnats mourn
  Among the river sallows, borne aloft
    Or sinking as the light wind lives or dies;
And full-grown lambs loud bleat from hilly bourn;
  Hedge-crickets sing; and now with treble soft
  The red-breast whistles from a garden-croft;
    And gathering swallows twitter in the skies.

JOHN KEATS

Autumn

I love the fitful gust that shakes
The casement all the day,
And from the glossy elm-tree takes
The faded leaves away,
Twirling them by the window pane
With thousand others down the lane.

I love to see the shaking twig
Dance till the shut of eve,
The sparrow on the cottage rig,
Whose chirp would make believe
That Spring was just now flirting by
In Summer's lap with flowers to lie.

I love to see the cottage smoke
Curl upwards through the trees,
The pigeons nestled round the cote
On November days like these:
The cock upon the dunghill crowing,
The mill-sails on the heath a-going.

The feather from the raven's breast
Falls on the stubble lea,
The acorns near the old crow's nest
Drop pattering down the tree:
The grunting pigs that wait for all,
Scramble and hurry where they fall.

JOHN CLARE

A Day in Autumn

It will not always be like this,
The air windless, a few last
Leaves adding their decoration
To the trees' shoulders, braiding the cuffs
Of the boughs with gold; a bird preening
In the lawn's mirror. Having looked up
From the day's chores, pause a minute,
Let the mind take its photograph
Of the bright scene, something to wear
Against the heart in the long cold.

R. S. THOMAS

October Dawn

October is marigold, and yet
A glass half full of wine left out

To the dark heaven all night, by dawn
Has dreamed a premonition

Of ice across its eye as if
The ice-age had begun its heave.

The lawn overtrodden and strewn
From the night before, and the whistling green

Shrubbery are doomed. Ice
Has got its spearhead into place.

First a skin, delicately here
Restraining a ripple from the air;

Soon plate and rivet upon pond and brook;
Then tons of chain and massive lock

To hold rivers. Then, sound by sight
Will Mammoth and Sabre-tooth celebrate

Reunion while a fist of cold
Squeezes the fire at the core of the world,

Squeezes the fire at the core of the heart,
And now it is about to start.

TED HUGHES

From, The Nature of Cold Weather

I

The moon stares for an instant, then a cloud lays
Flat on her mouth like a finger;
Over the acres of ground-leaves,
The spiking darts that were trees,
Again she steals upon them with her red.

II

Like a copper bowl burning before a fire,
She's red, and rouges the soused leaves
That take a mere street light and shoot it back in beams,
Or overcrust quietly in the colder dark.
The houses stuffed with light
Rest back on their oars of light
Over the dark flowing of the street.

PETER REDGROVE

Scotland's Winter

Now the ice lays its smooth claws on the sill,
The sun looks from the hill
Helmed in his winter casket,
And sweeps his arctic sword across the sky.
The water at the mill
Sounds more hoarse and dull.
The miller's daughter walking by
With frozen fingers soldered to her basket
Seems to be knocking
Upon a hundred leagues of floor
With her light heels, and mocking

Percy and Douglas dead,
And Bruce on his burial bed,
Where he lies white as may
With wars and leprosy,
And all the kings before
This land was kingless,
And all the singers before
This land was songless,
This land that with its dead and living waits the Judgement
   Day.
But they, the powerless dead,
Listening can hear no more
Than a hard tapping on the sounding floor
A little overhead
Of common heels that do not know
Whence they come or where they go
And are content
With their poor frozen life and shallow banishment.

EDWIN MUIR

Skating

From *The Prelude*

And in the frosty season, when the sun
Was set, and visible for many a mile
The cottage windows blazed through twilight gloom,
I heeded not their summons: happy time
It was indeed for all of us – for me
It was a time of rapture! Clear and loud
The village clock tolled six, – I wheeled about,
Proud and exulting like an untired horse
That cares not for his home. All shod with steel,
We hissed along the polished ice in games

Confederate, imitative of the chase
And woodland pleasures, – the resounding horn,
The pack loud chiming, and the hunted hare.
So through the darkness and the cold we flew,
And not a voice was idle; with the din
Smitten, the precipices rang aloud;
The leafless trees and every icy crag
Tinkled like iron; while far distant hills
Into the tumult sent an alien sound
Of melancholy not unnoticed, while the stars
Eastward were sparkling clear, and in the west
The orange sky of evening died away.
Not seldom from the uproar I retired
Into a silent bay, or sportively
Glanced sideways, leaving the tumultuous throng,
To cut across the reflex of a star
That fled, and, flying still before me, gleamed
Upon the glassy plain; and oftentimes,
When we had given our bodies to the wind,
And all the shadowy banks on either side
Came sweeping through the darkness, spinning still
The rapid line of motion, then at once
Have I, reclining back upon my heels,
Stopped short; yet still the solitary cliffs
Wheeled by me – even as if the earth had rolled
With visible motion her diurnal round!
Behind me did they stretch in solemn train,
Feebler and feebler, and I stood and watched
Till all was tranquil as a dreamless sleep.

WILLIAM WORDSWORTH

Creative Writing

1 What details do you associate with each of the four seasons?

Jot down, in rough, the phrase 'Spring is . . .' as the beginning of your poem. Then, try to write down *quickly* (each on a separate line) the sights, sounds, smells and activities which this season brings to mind.

Now try and make similar notes for the other three seasons: do not spend more than three or four minutes on each.

You may be able to use one or more sets of notes as the basis for a short poem.

2 Look at the photograph of the flower pushing its way through the snow (on p. 110).

What details stand out to you?

Are any comparisons suggested by the texture of the snow or the appearance of the flower?

Perhaps you can write a poem suggested by the picture.

3 In his description of skating on p. 111 Wordsworth conveys the excitement and atmosphere of this winter pastime. Perhaps you could try to do the same for other winter activities which you have experienced – sledging, snowballing, skiing, or sliding.

4 Constable's picture of *The Cornfield*, on p. 103, captures the atmosphere of a warm day in high summer. It is an easy picture to step into. Imagine yourself walking down the track. What do you see? What do you hear? What do you smell? What is the air like?

You may be able to write a poem using this picture as a starting-point.

5 The seasons are a traditional source of inspiration for haiku poems, partly because they provide many simple, striking images.

Perhaps you could write a haiku suggested by one of the following: the winter sun; winter trees; warm summer rain; first spring shoots (the picture on p. 110 may help); holly berries; fields of stubble.

If you are in doubt about the haiku form look back at p. 4.

CREATURES

The Fish

I caught a tremendous fish
and held him beside the boat
half out of water, with my hook
fast in the corner of his mouth.
He didn't fight.
He hadn't fought at all.
He hung a grunting weight,
battered and venerable
and homely. Here and there
his brown skin hung in strips
like ancient wall-paper,
and its pattern of darker brown
was like wall-paper:
shapes like full-blown roses
stained and lost through age.
He was speckled with barnacles,
fine rosettes of lime,
and infested
with tiny white sea-lice,
and underneath two or three
rags of green weed hung down.
While his gills were breathing in
the terrible oxygen
– the frightening gills
fresh and crisp with blood,
that can cut so badly –
I thought of the coarse white flesh
packed in like feathers,
the big bones and the little bones,

the dramatic reds and blacks
of his shiny entrails,
and the pink swim-bladder
like a big peony.
I looked into his eyes
which were far larger than mine
but shallower, and yellowed,
the irises backed and packed
with tarnished tinfoil
seen through the lenses
of old scratched isinglass.
They shifted a little, but not
to return my stare.
– It was more like the tipping
of an object toward the light.
I admired his sullen face,
the mechanism of his jaw,
and then I saw
that from his lower lip
– if you could call it a lip –
grim, wet and weapon-like,
hung five old pieces of fish-line,
or four and a wire leader
with the swivel still attached,
with all their five big hooks
grown firmly in his mouth.
A green line, frayed at the end
where he broke it, two heavier lines,
and a fine black thread
still crimped from the strain and snap
when it broke and he got away.
Like medals with their ribbons
frayed and wavering
a five-haired beard of wisdom
trailing from his aching jaw.
I stared and stared
and victory filled up

the little rented boat,
from the pool of bilge
where oil had spread a rainbow
around the rusted engine,
to the bailer rusted orange,
the sun-cracked thwarts,
the oarlocks on their strings,
the gunnels – until everything
was rainbow, rainbow, rainbow!
And I let the fish go.

ELIZABETH BISHOP

Old Wolf

lopes on purpose, paddling the snow
Of the soft-blown winterlocked landscape,
Under the loaded branches in the hush of forests.
Stops for its own reasons, shapeless
In the white shadows that have
Stopped breathing.
The prints run into the dark and
The stars wheel, circling the silence.

JAMES TAYLOR

The Runaway

Once when the snow of the year was beginning to fall,
We stopped by a mountain pasture to say, 'Whose colt?'
A little Morgan had one forefoot on the wall,
The other curled at his breast. He dipped his head
And snorted at us. And then he had to bolt.
We heard the miniature thunder where he fled,

And we saw him, or thought we saw him, dim and grey,
Like a shadow against the curtain of falling flakes.
'I think the little fellow's afraid of the snow.
He isn't winter-broken. It isn't play
With the little fellow at all. He's running away.
I doubt if even his mother could tell him, "Sakes,
It's only weather." He'd think she didn't know!
Where is his mother? He can't be out alone.'
And now he comes again with clatter of stone,
And mounts the wall again with whited eyes
And all his tail that isn't hair up straight.
He shudders his coat as if to throw off flies.
'Whoever it is that leaves him out so late,
When other creatures have gone to stall and bin,
Ought to be told to come and take him in.'

ROBERT FROST

A Bird Came Down the Walk

A bird came down the walk:
He did not know I saw;
He bit an angle-worm in halves
And ate the fellow, raw.

And then he drank a dew
From a convenient grass,
And then hopped sidewise to the wall
To let a beetle pass.

He glanced with rapid eyes
That hurried all abroad, –
They looked like frightened beads, I thought
He stirred his velvet head

Like one in danger; cautious,
I offered him a crumb,
And he unrolled his feathers
And rowed him softer home

Than oars divide the ocean,
Too silver for a seam,
Or butterflies, off banks of noon,
Leap, plashless, as they swim.

EMILY DICKINSON

Rookery

Here they come, freckling the sunset,
The slow big sailers bearing down
On the plantation. They have flown
Their sorties and are now well met.

The upper twigs dip and wobble
With each almost two-point landing,
Then ride to rest. There is nothing
Else to do now only settle.

But they keep up a guttural chat
As stragglers knock the roost see-saw.
Something's satisfied in that caw.
Who wouldn't come to rest like that?

SEAMUS HEANEY

The Fly

Little Fly,
Thy summer's play
My thoughtless hand
Has brushed away.

Am not I
A fly like thee?
Or art not thou
A man like me?

For I dance,
And drink, and sing,
Till some blind hand
Shall brush my wing.

If thought is life
And strength and breath,
And the want
Of thought is death;

Then am I
A happy fly,
If I live
Or if I die.

WILLIAM BLAKE

Aid

I almost popped underfoot
A shiny beetle like a boot
Its laces waving in the air
Not knowing how it was or where;

Being drunk, I had the knack
To know its feelings on its back;
I'd get my foot under its carapace
And shove it safely back to grass:
It might want to get there quick
To the damp grass to be sick
Or, plates creaking, unload its eggs.
I stood unsteady on my bottled legs
And raised one foot, as I have said:
But, to keep my balance, squashed its head.

Looking down, I held my breath
At this accidental death;
Scanning up and down the path,
I waited for descending wrath;
Then, keeping the ground beneath my feet
I strolled off home to eat,
Along the stony paths, leaf-strewn,
Whistling a sober little tune.

PETER REDGROVE

View of a Pig

The pig lay on a barrow dead.
It weighed, they said, as much as three men.
Its eyes closed, pink white eyelashes.
Its trotters stuck straight out.

Such weight and thick pink bulk
Set in death seemed not just dead.
It was less than lifeless, further off.
It was like a sack of wheat.

I thumped it without feeling remorse.
One feels guilty insulting the dead,
Walking on graves. But this pig
Did not seem able to accuse.

It was too dead. Just so much
A poundage of lard and pork.
Its last dignity had entirely gone.
It was not a figure of fun.

Too dead now to pity.
To remember its life, din, stronghold
Of earthly pleasure as it had been,
Seemed a false effort, and off the point.

Too deadly factual. Its weight
Oppressed me – how could it be moved?
And the trouble of cutting it up!
The gash in its throat was shocking, but not pathetic.

Once I ran at a fair in the noise
To catch a greased piglet
That was faster and nimbler than a cat,
Its squeal was the rending of metal.

Pigs must have hot blood, they feel like ovens.
Their bite is worse than a horse's –
They chop a half-moon clean out.
They eat cinders, dead cats.

Distinctions and admirations such
As this one was long finished with.
I stared at it a long time. They were going to scald it,
Scald it and scour it like a doorstep.

TED HUGHES

Dissection

This rat looks like it is made of marzipan
Soft and neatly packaged in its envelope;
I shake it free.
Fingering the damp, yellow fur, I know
That this first touch is far the worst.

 There is a book about it that contains
Everything on a rat, with diagrams
Meticulous, but free from blood
Or all the yellow juices
I will have to pour away.

 Now peg it out:
My pins are twisted and the board is hard
But, using force and fracturing its legs
I manage though
And crucify my rat.

 From the crutch to the throat the fur is ripped
Not neatly, not as shown in the diagrams,
But raggedly;
My hacking has revealed the body wall
As a sack that is fat with innards to be torn
By the inquisitive eye
And the hand that strips aside.

 Inside this taut, elastic sack is a surprise;
Not the chaos I had thought to find,
No oozing mash; instead of that
A firmly coiled discipline
Of overlapping liver, folded gut;
A neatness that is like a small machine –
And I wonder what it is that has left this rat,
Why a month of probing could not make it go again,
What it is that has disappeared . . .

 The bell has gone; it is time to go for lunch.
I fold the rat, replace it in its bag,
Wash from my hands the sweet

Smell of meat and formalin
And go and eat a meat pie afterwards.
   So, for four weeks or so, I am told
I shall continue to dissect this rat;
Like a child
Pulling apart a clock he cannot mend.

COLIN ROWBOTHAM

An Advancement of Learning

I took the embankment path
(As always, deferring
The bridge). The river nosed past,
Pliable, oil-skinned, wearing

A transfer of gables and sky.
Hunched over the railing,
Well away from the road now, I
Considered the dirty-keeled swans.

Something slobbered curtly, close,
Smudging the silence: a rat
Slimed out of the water and
My throat sickened so quickly that

I turned down the path in cold sweat
But God, another was nimbling
Up the far bank, tracing its wet
Arcs on the stones. Incredibly then

I established a dreaded
Bridgehead. I turned to stare
With deliberate, thrilled care
At my hitherto snubbed rodent.

126

He clockworked aimlessly a while,
Stopped, back bunched and glistening,
Ears plastered down on his knobbed skull,
Insidiously listening.

The tapered tail that followed him,
The raindrop eye, the old snout:
One by one I took all in.
He trained on me. I stared him out

Forgetting how I used to panic
When his grey brothers scraped and fed
Behind the hen-coop in our yard,
On ceiling boards above my bed.

This terror, cold, wet-furred, small-clawed,
Retreated up a pipe for sewage.
I stared a minute after him.
Then I walked on and crossed the bridge.

SEAMUS HEANEY

Cats

Cats are contradictions; tooth and claw
Velvet-padded;
Snowflake-gentle paw
A fist of pins;
Kettles on the purr
Ready to spit;
Black silk then bristled fur.

Cats are of the East –
Scimitar and sphinx;
Sunlight striped with shade.
Leopard, lion, lynx
Moss-footed in a frightened glade;
Slit-eyes an amber glint
Or boring through the darkness, cool as jade.

Cats have come to rest
Upon the cushioned West.
Here, dyed-in-the-silk,
They lap up bottled milk –
Not that of human kindness –
And return
To the mottled woods of Spring
Making the trees afraid
With leaf and wing
A-flutter at the movement in the fern.

Midnight-wild
With phosphorescent eyes,
Cats are morning-wise
Sleeping as they stare into the sun,
Blind to the light,
Deaf to echoing cries
From a ravaged wood.
Cats see black and white
Morning and night as one.

PHOEBE HESKETH

Cats

Cats no less liquid than their shadows
Offer no angles to the wind.
They slip, diminished, neat, through loopholes
Less than themselves; will not be pinned

To rules or routes for journeys; counter
Attack with non-resistance; twist
Enticing through the curving fingers
And leave an angered, empty fist.

They wait, obsequious as darkness
Quick to retire, quick to return;
Admit no aim or ethics; flatter
With reservations; will not learn

To answer to their names; are seldom
Truly owned till shot or skinned.
Cats no less liquid than their shadows
Offer no angles to the wind.

A. S. J. TESSIMOND

My Cat Jeoffry

For I will consider my cat Jeoffry.
For he is the servant of the Living God, duly and daily
serving Him.
For at the first glance of the Glory of God in the East he
worships in his way.
For is this done by wreathing his body seven times round
with elegant quickness.
For then he leaps up to catch the musk, which is the blessing
of God on his prayer.

For he rolls upon prank to work it in.

For having done duty, and received blessing, he begins to consider himself.

For this he performs in ten degrees.

For first he looks upon his forepaws to see if they are clean.

For secondly he kicks up behind to clear away there.

For thirdly he works it upon stretch with the forepaws extended.

For fourthly he sharpens his paws by wood.

For fifthly he washes himself.

For sixthly he rolls upon wash.

For seventhly he fleas himself, that he may not be interrupted upon the beat.

For eighthly he rubs himself a-gainst a post.

For ninthly he looks up for his instructions.

For tenthly he goes in quest of food.

For having considered God and himself he will consider his neighbour.

For if he meets another cat he will kiss her in kindness.

For when he takes his prey he plays with it to give it a chance.

For one mouse in seven escapes by his dallying.

For when his day's work is done his business more properly begins.

For he keeps the Lord's watch in the night against the Adversary.

For he counteracts the powers of darkness by his electrical skin and glaring eyes.

For he counteracts the Devil, who is death, by brisking about the life.

For in his morning orisons he loves the sun and the sun loves him.

For he is of the tribe of Tiger.

For the Cherub Cat is a term of the Angel Tiger.

For he has the subtlety and hiss of the serpent, which in goodness he suppresses.

For he will not do destruction, if he is well-fed, neither
will he spit without provocation.
For he purrs in thankfulness, when God tells him he's a
good Cat.
For he is an instrument for the children to learn bene-
volence upon.
For every house is incomplete without him and a blessing
is lacking in the spirit.
For the Lord commanded Moses concerning the cats at the
departure of the Children of Israel from Egypt.
For every family had one cat at least in the bag.
For the English cats are the best in Europe.
For he is the cleanest in the use of his forepaws of any
quadrupede.
For the dexterity of his defence is an instance of the love
of God to him exceedingly.
For he is the quickest to his mark of any creature.
For he is tenacious of his point.
For he is a mixture of gravity and waggery.
For he knows that God is his Saviour.
For there is nothing sweeter than his peace when at rest.
For there is nothing brisker than his life when in motion.
For he is of the Lord's poor and so indeed is he called by
benevolence perpetually – Poor Jeoffry! poor Jeoffry!
the rat has bit thy throat.
For I bless the name of the Lord Jesus that Jeoffry is
better.
For the divine spirit comes about his body to sustain it in
complete cat.
For his tongue is exceeding pure so that it has in purity
what it wants in music.
For he is docile and can learn certain things.
For he can set up with gravity which is patience upon
approbation.
For can fetch and carry, which is patience in employment.
For he can jump over a stick which is patience upon proof
positive.

For he can spraggle upon waggle at the word of command.
For he can jump from an eminence into his master's
bosom.
For he can catch the cork and toss it again.
For he is hated by the hypocrite and miser.
For the former is afraid of detection.
And the latter refuses the charge.
For he camels his back to bear the first notion of business.
For he is good to think on, if a man would express himself
neatly.
For he made a great figure in Egypt for his signal services.
For he killed the Ichneumon-rat very pernicious by land.
For his ears are so acute that they sting again.
For from this proceeds the passing quickness of his
attention.
For by stroking of him I have found out electricity.
For I perceive God's light about him both wax and fire.
For the electrical fire is the spiritual substance, which God
sends from heaven to sustain the bodies of both man and
beast.
For God has blessed him in the variety of his movements.
For, tho he cannot fly, he is an excellent clamberer.
For his motions upon the face of the earth are more than
any other quadrupede.
For he can tread to all the measures upon the music.
For he can swim for life.
For he can creep.

CHRISTOPHER SMART

The Hawk

On Sunday the hawk fell on Bigging
  And a chicken screamed
  Lost in its own little snowstorm.
And on Monday he fell on the moor
  And the Field Club
  Raised a hundred silent prisms.
And on Tuesday he fell on the hill
  And the happy lamb
  Never knew why the loud collie straddled him.
And on Wednesday he fell on a bush
  And the blackbird
  Laid by his little flute for the last time.
And on Thursday he fell on Cleat
  And peerie Tom's rabbit
  Swung in a single arc from shore to hill.
And on Friday he fell on a ditch
  But the rampant rat,
  That eye and that tooth, quenched his flame.
And on Saturday he fell on Bigging
  And Jock lowered his gun
  And nailed a small wing over the corn.

GEORGE MACKAY BROWN

Hawk

Things motionless were felt to move
  Downward; the hedges crawled
Down steep sun-molten banks to where
  The shrunken river sprawled:

133

Dark cloud-ravines of shadow flowed
Sheer down the dark wood's cliff;
Draped heavily in golden heat,
The limbs of air fell stiff:

And, threatening doom, the sky's concentrated will
Hung in one black speck, poised above the hill.
GEORGE ROSTREVOR HAMILTON

The Mallard

Brown-checked, neat as new spring tweed,
A mallard, wing-stretched in the sun,
Watched from the bank of a beer-bubble stream
Her ducklings, one after one,
Daring, dipping in dazzling weed,
Nuzzling joyful mud.
Black and yellow, downy as bees,
They busied about a fringe of reed
In a paddled nursery pool.

The mother, content, lay dry,
Relaxed her wings, slackened her throat,
Dared to close one bead-black eye
When swift as terror a lightning stoat
Forked and flashed upstream.

Spatter and splash of mother and young –
Feathered drops whirled in a storm of fear,
Water thrashed in flight.
A stone for the stoat – I flung it near
And stood alone, not knowing what fate
Lay crouched in wait, while the stillness there
Grew ominous and bright.
PHOEBE HESKETH

Mallard

Squawking they rise from reeds into the sun,
climbing like furies, running on blood and bone,
with wings like garden shears clipping the misty air,
four mallard, hard winged, with necks like rods
fly in perfect formation over the marsh.

Keeping their distance, gyring, not letting slip the air,
but leaping into it straight like hounds or divers,
they stretch out into the wind and sound their horns again.

Suddenly siding to a bank of air unbidden
by hand signal or morse message of command
down sky they plane, sliding like corks on a current,
designed so deftly that all air is advantage,

till, with few flaps, orderly as they left earth,
alighting among curlew they pad on mud.

REX WARNER

Upon the Snail

She goes but softly, but she goeth sure;
She stumbles not as stronger creatures do:
Her journey's shorter, so she may endure
Better than they which do much further go.

She makes no noise, but stilly seizeth on
The flower or herb appointed for her food,
The which she quietly doth feed upon,
While others range and gare, but find no good.

And though she doth but very softly go,
However 'tis not fast, nor slow, but sure;
And certainly they that do travel so,
The prize they do aim at, they do procure.
JOHN BUNYAN

Considering the Snail

The snail pushes through a green
night, for the grass is heavy
with water and meets over
the bright path he makes, where rain
has darkened the earth's dark. He
moves in a wood of desire,

pale antlers barely stirring
as he hunts. I cannot tell
what power is at work, drenched there
with purpose, knowing nothing.
What is a snail's fury? All
I think is that if later

I parted the blades above
the tunnel and saw the thin
trail of broken white across
litter, I would never have
imagined the slow passion
to that deliberate progress.
THOM GUNN

Creative Writing

1 The three poems about cats on pages 127 to 132 each describe different ways of looking at these creatures. You yourselves may have a cat; most of you, at one time or another, will have played with one, and you can probably suggest some reasons why people find them fascinating.

You may be able to write about one of the many different moods or habits of a cat: chasing a piece of string . . . playing with a ball . . . stalking a bird . . . lapping up milk . . . washing itself . . . sleeping . . . angry.

Whichever of these you choose, try to capture the details of the cat's movements, sounds, appearance, and feel of its fur.

2 Two of the poems we have printed, Ted Hughes' *View of a Pig* on p. 121 and P. Redgrove's *Aid* on p. 120, may remind you of occasions when you have come across a dead animal: perhaps a pet that has just died, a budgerigar, a dog, a cat; sheep or cattle (particularly after an epidemic); a nestling fallen from the nest; an insect which you have killed yourself.

If you are able to write about such a subject try to describe not only what you saw but also your feelings at the time.

3 Many animals are hunters. You will all have watched such every-day occurrences as a blackbird after worms, a spider ensnaring a fly, a cat stalking a bird. Some of you may have seen rarer sights — a hawk swooping on its prey, a fox after chickens, a pike darting after smaller fish.

Perhaps you could imagine one such incident in detail and des-cribe in a poem what you see.

4 On p. 118 you will find a photograph of a bird feeding nest-lings. In writing a poem suggested by this picture notice parti-cularly the many small details of the nest, the feathers and foliage. The picture may also set you thinking about the way wild creatures struggle for survival.

5 Look at the photograph of the hippopotamus on pages 122–23. What comparisons come to mind when you look at the texture of his skin? the size of his eyes and ears? the mud? Does he seem to you to have a particular character? What might he be thinking?

Perhaps the answers to some of these questions might provide material for a poem.

SCHOOL

A Boy's Head

In it there is a space-ship
and a project
for doing away with piano lessons.

And there is
Noah's ark,
which shall be first.

And there is
an entirely new bird,
an entirely new hare,
an entirely new bumble-bee.

There is a river
that flows upwards.

There is a multiplication table.

There is anti-matter.

And it just cannot be trimmed.

I believe
that only what cannot be trimmed
is a head.
There is much promise
in the circumstance
that so many people have heads.

MIROSLAV HOLUB
(*trans. I. Milner and G. Theiner*)

Schoolroom on a Wet Afternoon

The unrelated paragraphs of morning
Are forgotten now: the severed heads of kings
Rot by the misty Thames: the rose of York
And Lancaster are pressed between the leaves
Of history; negroes sleep in Africa.
The complexities of simple interest lurk
In inkwells and the brittle sticks of chalk:
Afternoon is come and English Grammar.

Rain falls as though the sky has been bereaved,
Stutters its inarticulate grief on glass
Of every lachrymose pane. The children read
Their books or make pretence of concentration,
Each bowed head seems bent in supplication
Or resignation to the fate that waits
In the unmapped forests of the future.
Is it their doomed innocence noon weeps for?

In each diminutive breast a human heart
Pumps out the necessary blood: desires,
Pains and ecstasies surfride each singing wave
Which breaks in darkness on the mental shores.
Each child is disciplined; absorbed and still
At his small desk. Yet lift the lid and see,
Amidst frayed books and pencils, other shapes:
Vicious rope, glaring blade, the gun cocked to kill.

VERNON SCANNELL

Last Lesson of the Afternoon

When will the bell ring, and end this weariness?
How long have they tugged the leash, and strained apart,
My pack of unruly hounds! I cannot start
Them again on a quarry of knowledge they hate to hunt,
I can haul them and urge them no more.

No longer now can I endure the brunt
Of the books that lie out on the desks; a full threescore
Of several insults of blotted pages, and scrawl
Of slovenly work that they have offered me.
I am sick, and what on earth is the good of it all?
What good to them or me, I cannot see!

                        So, shall I take
My last dear fuel of life to heap on my soul
And kindle my will to a flame that shall consume
Their dross of indifference; and take the toll
Of their insults in punishment? – I will not! –

I will not waste my soul and my strength for this.
What do I care for all that they do amiss!
What is the point of this teaching of mine, and of this
Learning of theirs? It all goes down the same abyss.

What does it matter to me, if they can write
A description of a dog, or if they can't?
What is the point? To us both, it is all my aunt!
And yet I'm supposed to care, with all my might.

I do not, and will not; they won't and they don't;
    and that's all!
I shall keep my strength for myself; they can keep
    theirs as well.
Why should we beat our heads against the wall
Of each other? I shall sit and wait for the bell.

D. H. LAWRENCE

Exercise Book

Two and two four
four and four eight
eight and eight sixteen ...
Once again! says the master
Two and two four
four and four eight
eight and eight sixteen.
But look! the lyre bird
high on the wing
the child sees it
the child hears it
the child calls it
Save me
play with me
bird!
So the bird alights
and plays with the child
Two and two four ...
Once again! says the master
and the child plays
and the bird plays too ...
Four and four eight
eight and eight sixteen
and twice sixteen makes what?
Twice sixteen makes nothing
least of all thirty-two
anyhow
and off they go
For the child has hidden
The bird in his desk
and all the children
hear its song
and all the children
hear the music

and eight and eight in their turn
off they go
and four and four and two and two
in their turn fade away
and one and one make neither one nor two
but one by one off they go.
And the lyre-bird sings
and the child sings
and the master shouts
When you've quite finished playing the fool!
But all the children
Are listening to the music
And the walls of the classroom
quietly crumble.
The window panes turn
once more to sand
the ink is sea
the desk is trees
the chalk is cliffs
and the quill pen
a bird again.

                                    PAUL DEHN

Timothy Winters

Timothy Winters comes to school
With eyes as wide as a football-pool,
Ears like bombs and teeth like splinters:
A blitz of a boy is Timothy Winters.

His belly is white, his neck is dark,
And his hair is an exclamation-mark.
His clothes are enough to scare a crow
And through his britches the blue winds blow.

142

When teacher talks he won't hear a word *why?*
And he shoots down dead the arithmetic-bird, *— What's he doing now?*
He licks the patterns off his plate *— starving*
And he's not even heard of the Welfare State. *— why signif?*

Timothy Winters has bloody feet *— no shoes*
And he lives in a house on Suez Street, *— Sounds ghastly but*
He sleeps in a sack on the kitchen floor . *any other*
And they say there aren't boys like him any more. . *signif*
——Who's say? *(Suez?)*
Old Man Winters likes his beer
And his missus ran off with a bombardier, *— uniform, glamour*
Grandma sits in the grate with a gin *—* *(ran off*
And Timothy's dosed with an aspirin. *— drugs* *with a*
soldier

The Welfare Worker lies awake
But the law's as tricky as a ten-foot snake, . *— can't put him*
So Timothy Winters drinks his cup . *into care*
And slowly goes on growing up. *full of contradictions*
implies?
At Morning Prayers the Master helves *old fashioned cup* *+ tortuous,*
For children less fortunate than ourselves, *of life?* *unmoved by*
And the loudest response in the room is when
Timothy Winters roars 'Amen!' *Irony*

So come one angel, come on ten:
Timothy Winters says 'Amen
Amen amen amen amen.' *?*
Timothy Winters, Lord,
                    Amen.
                    CHARLES CAUSLEY

143

Truant

Sing a song of sunlight
My pocket's full of sky –
A starling's egg for April,
Jay's feather for July;
And here's a thorn bush three bags full
Of drift-white wool!

They call him dunce, and yet he can discern
Each mouse-brown bird,
And call its name and whistle back its call,
And spy among the fern
Delicate movement of a furred
Fugitive creature hiding from the day.
Discovered secrets magnify his play
Into a vocation.

Laughing at education,
He knows where the redshank hides her nest, perceives
A reed-patch tremble when a coot lays siege
To water territory.
Nothing escapes his eye:
A ladybird
Slides like a blood-drop down a spear of grass;
The sapphire sparkle of a dragon fly
Redeems a waste of weeds.
Collecting acorns, telling the beads of the year
On yew tree berries, his mind's too full for speech.

Back in the classroom he can never find
Answers to dusty questions, yet could teach,
Deeper than blackboard knowledge,
Geometry of twigs
Scratched on a sunlit wall;
History in stones, and seasons
Told by the fields' calendar –
Living languages of Spring and Fall.

PHOEBE HESKETH

The Bully Asleep

One afternoon, when grassy
Scents through the classroom crept,
Bill Craddock laid his head
Down on his desk, and slept.

The children came round him;
Jimmy, Roger, and Jane;
They lifted his head timidly
And let it sink again.

'Look, he's gone sound asleep, Miss,'
Said Jimmy Adair;
'He stays up all the night, you see;
His mother doesn't care.'

'Stand away from him, children.'
Miss Andrews stooped to see.
'Yes, he's asleep; go on
With your writing, and let him be.'

'Now's a good chance!' whispered Jimmy;
And he snatched Bill's pen and hid it.
'Kick him under the desk, hard;
He won't know who did it.

145

Fill all his pockets with rubbish –
Paper, apple-cores, chalk.'
So they plotted, while Jane
Sat wide-eyed at their talk.

Not caring, not hearing
Bill Craddock he slept on;
Lips parted, eyes closed –
Their cruelty gone.

'Stick him with pins!' muttered Roger.
'Ink down his neck!' said Jim.
But Jane, tearful and foolish,
Wanted to comfort him.

JOHN WALSH

Creative Writing

1 John Walsh's poem *The Bully Asleep* on p. 145 describes the re-action of a class to the form bully. Have you encountered any bullies in your own school? Try to describe their appearance and behaviour and also ask yourself why they act as they do.

2 In the few minutes before the bell for the end of afternoon school most people begin to feel restless. What things show this? What do you notice about other people's movements? What sounds are you aware of? Does your attention wander? Where?

What is your reaction and that of the rest of the class to the bell itself?

What are your feelings on getting out of school?

What are the *particular* sights and sounds which create the atmosphere of bustle and activity at the end of *your* school day?

You may be able to write a poem about one or more of these aspects of the end of school.

3 M. Holub's poem, *A Boy's Head*, on p. 138 imagines some of the strange and varied things that take up space in a boy's mind. Perhaps you could write a sequel entitled *A Girl's Head*.

4 Look carefully at your desk lid. Possibly it is new and shiny but it is quite likely that on it there are marks, initials, doodles, 'train lines', blots and stains dating back over many years. What is the texture of the wood like? Why and when were the different marks made? If a minute insect were to make its way across this desk 'landscape' what features would it notice? What obstacles would it encounter? One or two of these questions may suggest ideas for a poem.

5 Most of you will, at one time or another, have seen a fight in a school playground. How do you become aware that there is a fight in progress? When you hurry over, what do you see? What do you hear? How do other people react? What are your feelings? Perhaps you could write a poem capturing the atmosphere of the incident.

WAR

The Send-Off

Down the close, darkening lanes they sang their way
To the siding-shed,
And lined the train with faces grimly gay.

Their breasts were stuck all white with wreath and spray
As men's are, dead.

Dull porters watched them, and a casual tramp
Stood staring hard,
Sorry to miss them from the upland camp.
Then, unmoved, signals nodded, and a lamp
Winked to the guard.

So secretly, like wrongs hushed-up, they went.
They were not ours:
We never heard to which front these were sent.

Nor there if they yet mock what women meant
Who gave them flowers.

Shall they return to beatings of great bells
In wild train-loads?
A few, a few, too few for drums and yells,
May creep back, silent, to village wells
Up half-known roads.

WILFRED OWEN

The Sentry

We'd found an old Boche dug-out, and he knew,
And gave us hell, for shell on frantic shell
Hammered on top, but never quite burst through.
Rain, guttering down in waterfalls of slime
Kept slush waist-high that, rising hour by hour,
Choked up the steps too thick with clay to climb.
What murk of air remained stank old, and sour
With fumes of whizz-bangs, and the smell of men
Who'd lived there years, and left their curse in the den,
If not their corpses. . . .
                    There we herded from the blast
Of whizz-bangs, but one found our door at last, –
Buffeting eyes and breath, snuffing the candles.
And thud! flump! thud! down the steep steps came thumping
And splashing in the flood, deluging muck –
The sentry's body; then, his rifle, handles
Of old Boche bombs, and mud in ruck on ruck.
We dredged him up, for killed, until he whined
'O sir, my eyes – I'm blind – I'm blind, I'm blind!'
Coaxing, I held a flame against his lids
And said if he could see the least blurred light
He was not blind; in time he'd get all right.
'I can't,' he sobbed. Eyeballs, huge-bulged like squids',
Watch my dreams still; but I forgot him there
In posting next for duty, and sending a scout
To beg a stretcher somewhere, and floundering about
To other posts under the shrieking air.

· · · · ·

149

Those other wretches, how they bled and spewed,
And one who would have drowned himself for good,–
I try not to remember these things now.
Let dread hark back for one word only: how
Half listening to that sentry's moans and jumps,
And the wild chattering of his broken teeth,
Renewed most horribly whenever crumps
Pummelled the roof and slogged the air beneath –
Through the dense din, I say, we heard him shout
'I see your lights!' But ours had long died out.

WILFRED OWEN

The Man He Killed

'Had he and I but met
    By some old ancient inn,
We should have sat us down to wet
    Right many a nipperkin!'[1]   [1]beer-mug

'But ranged as infantry,
    And staring face to face,
I shot at him as he at me,
    And killed him in his place.

'I shot him dead because –
    Because he was my foe,
Just so: my foe of course he was;
    That's clear enough; although

'He thought he'd list, perhaps,
    Off hand like – just as I –
Was out of work – had sold his traps –
    No other reason why.

'Yes; quaint and curious war is!
  You shoot a fellow down
You'd treat if met where any bar is,
  Or help to half-a-crown.'
THOMAS HARDY

Attack

At dawn the ridge emerges massed and dun
In the wild purple of the glow'ring sun,
Smouldering through spouts of drifting smoke that shroud
The menacing scarred slope; and, one by one,
Tanks creep and topple forward to the wire.
The barrage roars and lifts. Then, clumsily bowed
With bombs and guns and shovels and battle-gear,
Men jostle and climb to meet the bristling fire.
Lines of grey, muttering faces, masked with fear,
They leave their trenches, going over the top,
While time ticks blank and busy on their wrists,
And hope, with furtive eyes and grappling fists,
Flounders in mud. O Jesus, make it stop!
SIEGFRIED SASSOON

Counter-Attack

We'd gained our first objective hours before
While dawn broke like a face with blinking eyes,
Pallid, unshaved and thirsty, blind with smoke.
Things seemed alright at first. We held their line,
With bombers posted, Lewis guns well placed,
And clink of shovels deepening the shallow trench.
  The place was rotten with dead; green clumsy legs
  High-booted, sprawled and grovelled along the saps,
  And trunks, face downward, in the sucking mud,
  Wallowed like trodden sand-bags loosely filled;
  And naked sodden buttocks, mats of hair,
  Bulged, clotted heads slept in the plastering slime.
  And then the rain began – the jolly old rain!

A yawning soldier knelt against the bank,
Staring across the morning blear with fog;
He wondered when the Allemands would get busy;
And then, of course, they started with five-nines
Traversing, sure as fate, and never a dud.
Mute in the clamour of shells he watched them burst
Spouting dark earth and wire with gusts from hell,
While posturing giants dissolved in drifts of smoke.
He crouched and flinched, dizzy with galloping fear,
Sick for escape – loathing the strangled horror
And butchered, frantic gestures of the dead.

An officer came blundering down the trench:
'Stand-to and man the fire-step!' On he went...
Gasping and bawling, 'Fire-step... counter-attack!'
   Then the haze lifted. Bombing on the right
   Down the old sap: machine-guns on the left;
   And stumbling figures looming out in front.
   'O Christ, they're coming at us!' Bullets spat,
And he remembered his rifle... rapid fire...
And started blazing wildly... then a bang
Crumpled and spun him sideways, knocked him out
To grunt and wriggle: none heeded him; he choked
And fought the flapping veils of smothering gloom,
Lost in a blurred confusion of yells and groans...
Down, and down, and down, he sank and drowned,
Bleeding to death. The counter-attack had failed.

SIEGFRIED SASSOON

A Working Party

Three hours ago he blundered up the trench,
Sliding and poising, groping with his boots;
Sometimes he tripped and lurched against the walls
With hands that pawed the sodden bags of chalk.
He couldn't see the man who walked in front;
Only he heard the drum and rattle of feet
Stepping along barred trench boards, often splashing
Wretchedly where the sludge was ankle-deep.

Voices would grunt 'Keep to your right – make way!'
When squeezing past some men from the front-line:
White faces peered, puffing a point of red;
Candles and braziers glinted through the chinks
And curtain-flaps of dug-outs; then the gloom
Swallowed his sense of sight; he stooped and swore
Because a sagging wire had caught his neck.

155

A flare went up; the shining whiteness spread
And flickered upward, showing nimble rats
And mounds of glimmering sand-bags, bleached with rain;
Then the slow silver moment died in dark.
The wind came posting by with chilly gusts
And buffeting at corners, piping thin.
And dreary through the crannies; rifle-shots
Would split and crack and sing along the night,
And shells came calmly through the drizzling air
To burst with hollow bang below the hill.
Three hours ago he stumbled up the trench;
Now he will never walk that road again:
He must be carried back, a jolting lump
Beyond all need of tenderness and care.

He was a young man with a meagre wife
And two small children in a Midland town;
He showed their photographs to all his mates,
And they considered him a decent chap
Who did his work and hadn't much to say,
And always laughed at other people's jokes
Because he hadn't any of his own.

That night when he was busy at his job
Of piling bags along the parapet,
He thought how slow time went, stamping his feet
And blowing on his fingers, pinched with cold.
He thought of getting back by half-past twelve,
And tot of rum to send him warm to sleep
In draughty dug-out frowsty with the fumes
Of coke, and full of snoring weary men.

He pushed another bag along the top,
Craning his body outward; then a flare
Gave one white glimpse of No Man's Land and wire;
And as he dropped his head the instant split
His startled life with lead, and all went out.

SIEGFRIED SASSOON

Wirers

'Pass it along, the wiring party's going out' –
And yawning sentries mumble, 'Wirers going out.'
Unravelling; twisting; hammering stakes with muffled thud,
They toil with stealthy haste and anger in their blood.

The Boche sends up a flare. Black forms stand rigid there,
Stock-still like posts; then darkness, and the clumsy ghosts
Stride hither and thither, whispering, tripped by
     clutching snare
Of snags and tangles.
                    Ghastly dawn with vaporous coasts
Gleams desolate along the sky, night's misery ended.

Young Hughes was badly hit; I heard him carried away,
Moaning at every lurch; no doubt he'll die today.
But *we* can say the front-line wire's been safely mended.

SIEGFRIED SASSOON

The Battle

Helmet and rifle, pack and overcoat
Marched through a forest. Somewhere up ahead
Guns thudded. Like the circle of a throat
The night on every side was turning red.

They halted and they dug. They sank like moles
Into the clammy earth between the trees.
And soon the sentries, standing in their holes,
Felt the first snow. Their feet began to freeze.

At dawn the first shell landed with a crack.
Then shells and bullets swept the icy woods.
This lasted many days. The snow was black.
The corpses stiffened in their scarlet hoods.

Most clearly of that battle I remember
The tiredness in eyes, how hands looked thin
Around a cigarette, and the bright ember
Would pulse with all the life there was within.

LOUIS SIMPSON

Old Soldier

A dream of battle on a windy night
Has wakened him. The shadows move once more
With rumours of alarm. He sees the height
And helmet of his terror in the door.

The guns reverberate; a livid arc
From sky to sky lightens the windowpanes
And all his room. The clock ticks in the dark;
A cool wind stirs the curtains, and it rains.

He lies remembering: 'That's how it was . . .'
And smiles, and drifts into a youthful sleep
Without a care. His life is all he has,
And that is given to the guards to keep.

LOUIS SIMPSON

Night Patrol

We sail at dusk. The red moon,
Rising in a paper lantern, sets fire
To the water, the black headland disappears,
Sullen in shadow, clenched like a paw.

The docks grow flat, rubbered with mist.
Cranes, like tall drunks, hang
Over the railway. The unloading of coal
Continues under blue arc-lights.

Turning south, the moon like a rouged face
Between masts, the knotted aerials swing
Taut against the horizon, the bag
Of sea crumpled in the spray-flecked blackness.

Towards midnight the cold stars, high
Over Europe, freeze on the sky,
Stigmata above the flickering lights
Of Holland. Flashes of gunfire

Lick out over meditative coastlines, betraying
The stillness. Taking up position, night falls
Exhausted about us. The wakes
Of gunboats sew the green dark with speed.

From Dunkirk red flames open fanwise
In spokes of light; like the rising moon
Setting fire to the sky, the remote
Image of death burns on the water.

The slow muffle of hours. Clouds grow visible.
Altering course the moon congeals on a new
Bearing. Northwards again, and Europe recedes
With the first sharp splinters of dawn.

The orange sky lies over the harbour,
Derricks and pylons like scarecrows
Black in the early light. And minesweepers
Pass us, moving out slowly to the North Sea.

ALAN ROSS

Air Raid across the Bay at Plymouth

I
Above the whispering sea
And waiting rocks of black coast,
Across the bay, the searchlight beams
Swing and swing back across the sky.

Their ends fuse in a cone of light
Held for a bright instant up
Until they break away again
Smashing that image like a cup.

II
Delicate aluminium girders
Project phantom aerial masts
Swaying crane and derrick
Above the sea's just lifting deck.

III
Triangles, parallels, parallelograms,
Experiment with hypotheses
On the blackboard sky,
Seeking that X
Where the enemy is met.
Two beams cross
To chalk his cross.

IV
A sound, sounding ragged, unseen
Is chased by two swords of light.
A thud. An instant when the whole night gleams.
Gold sequins shake out of a black-silk screen.

V
Jacob ladders slant
Up to the god of war
Who, from his heaven-high car,
Unloads upon a star
A destroying star.

Round the coast, the waves
Chuckle between rocks.
In the fields the corn
Sways, with metallic clicks.
Man hammers nails in Man,
High on his crucifix.
STEPHEN SPENDER

Grass

Pile the bodies high at Austerlitz and Waterloo.
Shovel them under and let me work –
                I am the grass; I cover all.

And pile them high at Gettysburg
And pile them high at Ypres and Verdun.
Shovel them under and let me work.
Two years, ten years, and passengers ask the conductor:
What place is this?
Where are we now?

I am the grass.
Let me work.

CARL SANDBURG

The Fly

She sat on a willow-trunk
watching
part of the battle of Crécy,
the shouts,
the gasps,
the groans,
the tramping and the tumbling.

During the fourteenth charge
of the French cavalry
she mated
with a brown-eyed male fly
from Vadincourt.

She rubbed her legs together
as she sat on a disembowelled horse
meditating
on the immortality of flies.

With relief she alighted
on the blue tongue
of the Duke of Clervaux.

163

When silence settled
and only the whisper of decay
softly circled the bodies

and only
a few arms and legs
still twitched jerkily under the trees,

she began to lay her eggs
on the single eye
of Johann Uhr,
the Royal Armourer.

And thus it was
that she was eaten by a swift
fleeing
from the fires of Estrées.

MIROSLAV HOLUB

(Trans. I. Milner and G. Theiner)

Creative Writing

None of you will have experienced a war, yet, through the speed of modern communications, none of you will have escaped second-hand contact with wars through television and newspapers. Some of you will be keen on war stories and, either through books or films, will know about a few of the more glamorous exploits and, maybe, something of the suffering of the two world wars. The fascination which the subject of war has for many people lies, perhaps, in the mixture of excitement and horror: it is an extreme situation which produces extreme emotions. The frequency with which sharp-eyed cameramen bring pictures of the latest slaughters into everyone's living-room gives us a dangerous familiarity with the horrors of war: dangerous, because with television or press pictures we are, except on rare occasions, uninvolved in what is happening. A passing feeling of 'how dreadful', a temporary concern for those who suffer – these are the reactions that we usually muster – for we have seen it so often before and it is happening so far away. It has nothing to do with us. Vietnam and Biafra take their place as unreal fictions alongside the Western and the thriller.

The value of reading the poems we have printed here and in attempting to put down your own thoughts and feelings about war is partly that these things act as correctives to this danger: war becomes a fact we have to face. In your own writing you can attempt to come to terms with this terrible subject in various ways. Here are some suggestions:

1 The group of First World War poems by Owen and Sassoon will give you some insight into the world of trench warfare. You may be able to put yourself in the place of one of the soldiers and write about your experiences. The painting entitled *Paths of Glory* on pages 152 and 153 may suggest something of the horror of this kind of war.

2 Talk to your parents and grandparents about how the Second World War affected them. Some may have been on active service abroad but most people will have seen a different side to war: rationbooks...queues for food, toys, or clothing...gas-masks...the Home-Guard...blackout...air-raid sirens... searchlights . . . air-raid shelters . . . bombed areas . . . evacuation...the blitz...'Lord Haw-Haw'. Perhaps, as a result of

165

your talk, you may be able to write about how the war affected your own family and neighbourhood. The painting entitled *Lens Bombed* on p. 166 although a First World War picture – may help you to appreciate the nightmare reality of civilian bombing.

3 Most of you, at one time or another, will have seen weapons of war on show. Some of you will have been to air displays and seen fighter planes, bombers, perhaps even guided missiles; others of you may have seen tanks on manoeuvres or warships and submarines in port.

Perhaps you could describe one of these weapons in detail and think about its purpose.

4 Look at the photograph on p. 158. It was taken during the Korean War and shows two American servicemen in action. Their indifference to the corpse and the expression on their faces may suggest to you the thoughts and feelings of men in battle. Try to write about this.

Index of First Lines

169

170

171

Index of Authors

172

Sources and Acknowledgements

Thanks are due to the authors (or their executors), their representatives and publishers mentioned in the following list for their kind permission to reproduce copyright material:

Jacques Prévert: 'To Paint the Portrait of a Bird' from *Paroles*, transl. Lawrence Ferlinghetti, Penguin Books Ltd.

A. Moritake: 'Fallen Flower' from *Penguin Book of Japanese Verse*, transl. G. Bownas and A. Thwaite, Penguin Books Ltd.

Z. Herbert: 'The Pebble' from *Penguin Selection*, transl. C. Milosz and P. Dale Scott, Penguin Books Ltd.

Yuan Mei: 'Expression of Feelings VII' from *Penguin Book of Chinese Verse*, transl. R. Kotewall and N. L. Smith, Penguin Books Ltd.

Miroslav Holub: 'The Fly' and 'A Boy's Head' and 'In the Microscope' from *Penguin Selected Poems*, transl. I Milner and G. Theiner, Penguin Books Ltd.

Rex Warner: 'Mallard' from *Poems and Contradictions*, The Bodley Head Ltd.

Peter Redgrove: 'Gallows Bird' and 'Aid' from *The Collector and Other Poems*, and 'The Nature of Cold Weather, Parts I and II' and 'Spring' from *The Nature of Cold Weather*, Routledge & Kegan Paul Ltd.

Paul Dehn: 'Exercise Book' from *The Fern on the Rock*, copyright © 1965 (from the French of Jacques Prévert), Hamish Hamilton, London.

George MacBeth: 'The Bird' from *The Broken Places*, Scorpion Press.

Edwin Brock: 'A Moment of Respect' from *With Love from Judas*, Scorpion Press.

Edward Lucie-Smith: 'The Lesson' from *A Tropical Childhood and Other Poems*, by permission of the Oxford University Press.

Thomas Hardy: 'The Oxen', 'The Man He Killed' and 'Epitaph on a Pessimist' from *Collected Poems by Thomas Hardy*, by permission of the Trustees of the Hardy Estate and Macmillan & Co. Ltd.

William Carlos Williams: 'A Negro Woman' from *Pictures from Breughel* and 'Approach to a City' from *Collected Later Poems*, MacGibbon & Kee Ltd.

e. e. cummings: 'nobody loses all the time' from *Complete Poems*, MacGibbon & Kee Ltd.

Alan Ross: 'Night Patrol' from *Poems 1942–67*, Eyre & Spottiswoode (Publishers) Ltd.

D. H. Lawrence: 'Bare Almond Trees', 'The Optimist', 'Last Lesson in the Afternoon' and extracts from 'Storm in the Black Forest', 'Snake', 'Fish' and 'Kangaroo' from *The Complete Poems of D. H. Lawrence*, Laurence Pollinger Ltd. and the Estate of the late Mrs. Frieda Lawrence.

L. A. G. Strong: 'A Priest' and 'Matthew Bird' from *The Body's Imperfection*, Methuen & Co. Ltd.

Po Chu'I: 'The Red Cockatoo' from *170 Chinese Poems*, transl. Arthur Waley, Constable Publishers.

Emily Dickinson: 'A Bird Came Down the Walk', reprinted by permission of the publishers and the Trustees of Amherst College from Thomas H. Johnson, Editor, *The Poems of Emily Dickinson*, Cambridge, Mass.: The Belknap Press of Harvard University Press, Copyright, 1951, 1955, by The President and Fellows of Harvard College.

George Mackay Brown: 'The Hawk' from *The Year of the Whale*, The Hogarth Press Ltd.

Wilfred Owen: 'The Send Off' and 'The Sentry' from *The Collected Poems of Wilfred Owen*, Mr. Harold Owen and Chatto and Windus Ltd.

Elizabeth Bishop: 'The Fish' from *Selected Poems*, Chatto and Windus Ltd.

Vernon Scannell: 'Gunpowder Plot', 'Autobiographical Note' and 'Schoolroom on a Wet Afternoon'.

A. S. J. Tessimond: 'Cats' from *Selection*, Putnam & Co. Ltd. and Hubert Nicholson, literary executor to the late A. S. J. Tessimond.

Charles Causley: 'Timothy Winters' from *Union Street*, Rupert Hart-Davis Ltd.

R. S. Thomas: 'Epitaph' and 'A Day in Autumn' from *Poetry for Supper* and 'Farm Child' and 'Depopulation of the Hills' from *Song at the Year's Turning*, Rupert Hart-Davis Ltd.

Phoebe Hesketh: 'Going Away and Returning', 'Cats', 'The Mallard' and 'Truant' from *Prayer for the Sun*, Rupert Hart-Davis Ltd.

Anthony Thwaite: 'The Pond' from *The Stones of Emptiness*, by permission of the Oxford University Press.

Hart Crane: 'March' from *The Complete Poems and Selected Letters and Prose*, by permission of the Oxford University Press.

Theodore Roethke: 'Flower Dump' from *Words for the Wind*, Martin Secker & Warburg Ltd.

H. G. Henderson: 'I Wonder', 'Springtime Rain', 'Flower-Viewing', 'The Apprentice Priestling', 'The Poor Man's Son', 'The Weeping Willow', 'A Wish', 'The Cuckoo's Song', 'City People', 'The Dragonfly' and 'Constancy' from *An Introduction to Haiku* by Harold G. Henderson, copyright © 1958 by Harold G. Henderson, reprinted by permission of Doubleday & Company, Inc.

Ogden Nash: 'Lather As You Go' from *Family Reunion*, J. M. Dent & Sons Ltd.

John Betjeman: 'Slough' from *Collected Poems*, John Murray Ltd.

Robert Frost: 'Acquainted with the Night', 'Nothing Gold Can Stay' and 'The Runaway' from *The Complete Poems of Robert Frost*, Jonathan Cape Ltd. and Holt, Rinehart and Winston, Inc.

Stephen Spender: 'Air Raid Across The Bay at Plymouth' from *Collected Poems*, Faber & Faber Ltd.

Ezra Pound: 'In A Station of the Metro', 'Fan Piece for her Imperial Lord', 'Liu Ch'E' and 'Ts'Ai Chi'H' from *Collected Shorter Poems*, Faber & Faber Ltd.

Norman Nicholson: 'From a Boat at Coniston', 'The Motion of the

Earth'. 'The Oak Tree' and an extract from 'Mountain Limestone' all from *The Pot Geranium*, Faber & Faber Ltd.

Louis MacNeice: 'Reflections' and 'Corner Seat' from *Collected Poems*, Faber & Faber Ltd.

Ted Hughes: 'Wind' and 'October Dawn' from *The Hawk in the Rain*, 'View of a Pig' and 'To Paint a Water Lily' from *Lupercal*, and 'Full Moon and Little Frieda' and 'Her Husband' from *Wodwo*, Faber & Faber Ltd.

Seamus Heaney: 'Cow in Calf', 'The Diviner', 'Blackberry-Picking', 'An Advancement of Learning' and extracts from 'Death of a Naturalist', 'Waterfall' and 'Docker' from *Death of a Naturalist*, Faber & Faber Ltd.; 'Rookery', *The Listener*; 'May Day', *New Statesman*.

Edwin Muir: 'Scotland's Winter' from *Collected Poems 1921–1958*, Faber & Faber Ltd.

Thom Gunn: 'Considering the Snail' from *My Sad Captains*, Faber & Faber Ltd.

Robert Graves: 'Love Without Hope' and 'The Beach' from *Collected Poems 1965*, A. P. Watt & Son.

Siegfried Sassoon: 'Blind', 'Wirers', 'A Working Party', 'Counter-Attack' and 'Attack' from *Collected Poems*, Mr. George Sassoon, executor of the late Siegfried Sassoon.

Edward Thomas: 'Cock-Crow' from *Collected Poems*, Mrs. Myfanwy Thomas.

May Swenson: 'Water Picture', copyright © 1965 May Swenson, first published in *The New Yorker*, reprinted by permission of Charles Scribner's Sons from *To Mix With Time* by May Swenson.

Louis Simpson: 'Old Soldier' from *A Dream of Governors* by Louis Simpson, copyright © 1959 by Louis Simpson, reprinted by permission of Wesleyan University Press; 'The Battle', reprinted by permission of Charles Scribner's Sons from *Good News of Death and Other Poems* by Louis Simpson, copyright 1955 Louis Simpson (*Poets of Today II*).

Carl Sandburg: 'Grass' from *Cornhuskers*, Jonathan Cape Ltd. and Holt, Rinehart and Winston Inc.

James Reeves: 'The Happy Boy' and 'Leaving Town' from *Collected Poems* William Heinemann Ltd.

George Rostrevor Hamilton: 'Hawk' from *Collected Poems and Epigrams*, William Heinemann Ltd.

Raymond Tong: 'African Beggar'.

James Kirkup: 'Tea in a Space Ship', 'A House in Summer', 'Earthquake' and 'The Equilibrist' by permission of the author; 'A Last Narcissus' from *Refusal to Conform*, by permission of the Oxford University Press.

T. S. Eliot: extract from 'The Love Song of J. Alfred Prufrock' from *The Collected Poems of T. S. Eliot*, Faber & Faber Ltd.

Sylvia Plath: 'Mushrooms' from *The Colossus* and 'Wuthering Heights', both by courtesy of Miss Olwyn Hughes.

Wole Soyinka: 'Season' from *Modern Poetry from Africa*, by courtesy of Mrs. O. Soyinka.

The Authors wish to thank the following for permission to reproduce photographs:

Museo del Prado, Madrid: 'Still Life', Melendez.
Kunsthistorisches Museum, Vienna: 'Der Winter', Arcimboldo.
The British Museum: 'Storm at Shono', Hokusai.
The Mansell Collection: 'The Cornfield', Constable.
Philadelphia Museum of Art: 'Lens Bombed', Otto Dix.
Imperial War Museum: 'Paths of Glory', Nevinson, by courtesy of the Trustees of the Imperial War Museum.
T. W. Lomax: 'Setting-sun, Receding tide'.
Mogens Carrebye: 'Reflection of trees in an old man's glasses', from the Beatles' film *The Fool on the Hill.*
Adolf Morath: 'Lancashire coalminer'.
Photographic Information Council: 'November the Fifth', by courtesy of the Photographic Information Council, Junior Photographers of the Year 1968.
Mt. Wilson and Palomar Observatories: 'Moon, region of Copernicus'.
R. D. Leakey: 'Stalactites in Simpson's Pot'.
R. Smithies and The Guardian: 'Cranes'.
Tony McGrath and The Observer: 'Nottingham street scene'.
United Press International: 'Freaks of Winter'.
R. A. Haynes: 'Hippopotamus'.
The Guardian: 'Nestlings'.
David Douglas Duncan: 'Two U.S. soldiers in action during the Korean War'.

We wish to thank our mother and our wives for the very considerable help they have given in the preparation of the typescript.

M.G.B.
P.B.